LIFE IN THE UNIVERSE

MICHAEL WILLIAM OVENDEN, a member of the staff of the Department of Astronomy of the University of Glasgow, Scotland, has delivered many lectures to lay audiences in Scotland and England on the subjects of astronomy and the position of life in relation to recent discoveries in the several sciences. This book is an outgrowth of a series of lectures he gave at Greenock, Scotland, and is adapted from articles that appeared originally in *The Illustrated London News*.

Dr. Ovenden, now 35, became interested in astronomy at the age of 10 and has been a member of the British Astronomical Association since he was 17. He received a B.Sc. degree with honors in physics from London University, his M.A. degree from Cambridge University and his Ph.D. degree from London University. He has been on the staff of the Department of Astronomy of The Observatories, University of Cambridge, and, in 1961, was a visiting staff member of the Dominion Astrophysical Observatory in Victoria, British Columbia, where he carried on research with its 73-inch telescope.

Dr. Ovenden has written papers for various technical publications and, in 1951–52, was editor of *The Observer*, a scientific journal. He is the author of *Looking at the Stars* (Phoenix House Ltd., 1957) and *Artificial Satellites* (Penguin Books Ltd., 1961). His popular writings on science have appeared also in *Discovery* and *Science Progress*, as well as *The Illustrated London News*. He became a fellow of the Royal Astronomical Society in 1945 and has been its secretary since 1957, was secretary of the British Astronomical Association in 1946 and vice-president in 1951 and is a member of the International Astronomical Union.

LIFE
IN
THE UNIVERSE
A Scientific Discussion

MICHAEL W. OVENDEN

Published by Anchor Books
Doubleday & Company, Inc.
Garden City, New York

ILLUSTRATIONS BY ROBERT L. KELLEY
TYPOGRAPHY BY SUSAN SIEN

THE SCIENCE STUDY SERIES

The Science Study Series offers to students and to the general public the writing of distinguished authors on the most stirring and fundamental topics of science, from the smallest known particles to the whole universe. Some of the books tell of the role of science in the world of man, his technology and civilization. Others are biographical in nature, telling the fascinating stories of the great discoverers and their discoveries. All the authors have been selected both for expertness in the fields they discuss and for ability to communicate their special knowledge and their own views in an interesting way. The primary purpose of these books is to provide a survey within the grasp of the young student or the layman. Many of the books, it is hoped, will encourage the reader to make his own investigations of natural phenomena.

The Series, which now offers topics in all the sciences and their applications, had its beginning in a project to revise the secondary schools' physics curriculum. At the Massachusetts Institute of Technology during 1956 a group of physicists, high school teachers, journalists, apparatus designers, film producers, and other specialists organized the Physical Science Study Committee, now operating as a part of Educational Services Incorporated, Watertown, Massachusetts. They pooled their knowledge and experience toward the design and creation of aids to the learning of physics. Initially their effort was supported by the National Science Foundation, which has continued to aid the program. The Ford Foundation, the Fund for the Advancement of Education, and the Alfred P. Sloan Foundation have also given support. The Committee has created a textbook, an extensive film series, a laboratory guide, especially designed apparatus, and a teacher's source book.

The Series is guided by a Board of Editors consisting of Bruce F. Kingsbury, Managing Editor; John H. Durston, General Editor; Paul F. Brandwein, the Conservation Foundation and Harcourt, Brace & World, Inc.; Francis L. Friedman, Massachusetts Institute of Technology; Samuel A. Goudsmit, Brookhaven National Laboratory; Philippe LeCorbeiller, Harvard University; Gerard Piel, *Scientific American*; and Herbert S. Zim, Simon and Schuster, Inc.

CONTENTS

LIFE IN THE UNIVERSE

I. LIFE AND THE UNIVERSE

The earliest civilizations that grew up in the valleys of the great rivers in Mesopotamia, millennia before the Christian era, had what seem to us to be ridiculous ideas of the nature of the Universe. Earth (i.e., matter), they supposed, was born of the merging of salt water and fresh water—because they could see the silting up of their rivers at the mouth of the Persian Gulf. They saw the pattern of evolution of the Universe in terms of the clash of personal powers—because this was how their own societies changed. In attempting to understand the Universe, they were drawing upon the only experiences that they had, experiences as human beings in a changing society. (After all, in speaking of *laws* of nature, are we not likewise seeing a correspondence between the world and human society?) Primitive as these cosmologies were, they were true ancestors of modern science. For we must not forget that, in the end, science is a human activity, and the way of its progress depends es-

sentially upon the particular situation of human beings in the Universe.

Science is not only a matter of collecting data for a
description of the world—it is also, and more fundamentally, an attempt to gain insight into or understanding of the structure and working of the Universe.
Basically, science attempts to understand the Universe by drawing analogies between the unfamiliar
world revealed by scientific experiment or observation
and the familiar world of everyday experience. A
single example will suffice to illustrate this point. A
very wide range of experiments on the behavior of
gases could be understood quantitatively by suppos-
ing that a gas consists of millions upon millions of
atoms or molecules that behave like tiny billiard balls.
So powerful was this concept that it was easy for some
scientists at the end of the last century to forget that
it was, in the end, the drawing of an analogy between
the invisible atomic world and the world of our everyday senses; they came to believe that atoms were
really small, hard elastic spheres. With the rise of
modern atomic physics, experiments showed clearly
that it was only in some respects that atoms could be
likened to billiard balls; in other respects their properties were quite different. A new picture arose, of an
atom consisting of an electrically charged nucleus,
and a number of oppositely charged electrons revolv-
ing around it like tiny planets around a tiny sun. For
a while the electrons and nuclei could be thought of
as small bits of matter, but further experiments
showed that this newer picture did not tell all the
story, for while in some circumstances the electron be-

haves like a particle, in other circumstances it behaves like a wave.

Throughout, the important word "like" keeps cropping up, for all these theories are analogies, and it is meaningless to ask whether an atom really is a tiny ball, or whether an electron really is a wave. And the further we go from everyday experience, either into the world of the very small or into the world of the very large, the less direct will be the analogies that we draw. But do not suppose that because science cannot answer, in any final or complete form, the question "What is the Universe *really* like?" that scientific theories are useless. They are not. They enable us to see patterns of relationship between apparently widely diverse phenomena—the brightness of a star can be related to the structure of the hydrogen atom, for example—and to make predictions about the results of future experiments or observations. It is precisely because science is willing to change the analogy as the range of our experience of the Universe widens that it is a *progressive* discipline.

It is the situation of human beings in the Universe that I will try to explore in this book. Such an exploration is bound to be a very personal one, and my own interests as an astronomer will color the picture that I paint. Scientists from other disciplines, or scholars from other philosophies, would place emphasis in other ways. But I believe that, no matter what specialty he selects for study, an intelligent man must come in the end to reflect upon the human situation as he sees it. I hope that my own reflections, personal though they may be, will not be without interest.

A central question will lie behind much of the
forthcoming discussion: "Is life (and especially intelligent life) a rare by-product of processes occurring
in a Universe that is at best indifferent to life, or may
we expect it to be a reasonably widespread manifestation?" It is true that, biologically speaking, life is a
process of chemical reaction occurring among large
molecules. As such, it could not exist on the surfaces,
still less in the interiors, of the stars, which are too hot
for such molecules to exist intact; nor could such
chemical reactions proceed at all rapidly at the low
temperatures of interstellar space (although the use
of the word "rapidly" implies a comparison with human life). But, while it may be true that life is possible only on a planet at a suitable distance from a
star, we must beware of adopting a medieval attitude
that the Earth is the measure of the Universe. For
life has adapted itself, by evolution, to a wide range
of conditions on the Earth: what limits can we set to
its ability to adapt itself to a more widely diverse environment?

Sizes in the Universe

With these thoughts in mind, I will begin with a
summary of the present picture of the physical Universe. At once, the astronomer is faced with the difficulty of communicating to his reader the immense distances that he meets in studying the Universe, distances that dwarf our everyday experience, and defy
our direct intuition. In this respect, the astronomer is

no different from other mortals. It is best to proceed, step by step, by a series of models.

If the earth were shrunk to the size of a pinhead

the sun at the same scale would be 6" in diameter and would be 50 ft. away from the earth.

Jupiter, our largest planet, would be ½" in dia. and 250 ft. away from the sun.

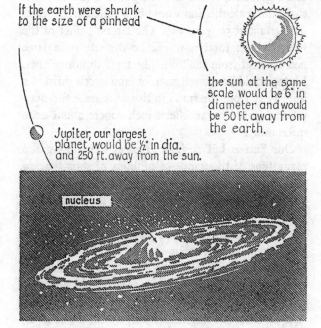

nucleus

Fig. 1. *The immensity of the Universe dwarfs the distances of our everyday experience. Our Sun orbits far from the nucleus of our Galaxy and is not particularly impressive among the tens of thousands of millions of other suns.*

In these days of jet air travel, the size of the Earth is within the comprehension of the seasoned traveler. I frequently travel from Scotland to the south coast of England by car, a distance of about 500 miles; I can see this distance on a one-foot globe of the Earth, and can appreciate the size of the Earth from direct experience. Suppose, then, that the Earth be shrunk, in imagination, to the size of a pinhead (Fig. 1). On the same scale the Sun would be a sphere 6 inches in diameter and 50 feet away. The largest planet of the solar system, Jupiter, would be the size of a large pea 250 feet from the Sun. The most distant planet, Pluto, would be a small grain of sand over a third of a mile away from the sun. On the same scale the nearest star would be another 6-inch sphere about 2000 miles away.

Our Sun is but a single, typical star among the many tens of thousands of millions of stars that go to make up our Galaxy; there are many more stars in our Galaxy than there are people on the Earth. Suppose that the Galaxy is shrunk, in imagination, to the size of the Earth. Then, on the same scale, the Sun would be a speck of dust about a fiftieth of a millimeter across. The stars would, on the average, be separated by a third of a mile, and would be other specks of dust of various sizes. Actually, the largest stars on this scale might be nearly a centimeter in diameter and if placed where the Sun is would engulf the Earth's orbit, while the smallest would be seen only with a microscope. The largest stars are red, cool stars (surface temperatures about 2000 degrees C), and are so tenuous that their densities are less than that of a good laboratory vacuum. The smallest are the hot White Dwarfs, so dense that a matchbox full of White Dwarf stuff would weigh a ton. Between the stars space is filled with an even more tenuous material that in places collects into interstellar dust and gas clouds. It is from this interstellar matter that stars are believed to condense.

Our Galaxy is but a single typical galaxy among many millions of such systems that can be observed with our large telescopes. They seem to be scattered through space more or less at random, with their distances apart being, on the average, about fifty times their diameters. They show a tendency to occur in clumps, or clusters, and there is some suggestion that galaxies may form higher-order systems, or supergalaxies. Just as the Earth moves around the Sun (in one year) and holds a balance between its tendency to fly off in a straight line (its inertia) and its tendency to fall into the Sun because of the Sun's gravitational pull, so the Sun moves around the center of the Galaxy (in a period of about 200 million years) and, possibly, galaxies move around the centers of supergalaxies in orbits of even longer periods.

Cosmic Time Scales

In astronomy we have to consider not only great distances but also long times. The description of the Universe you have read in the last several sentences gives no idea of the fact that the Universe is constantly changing (in its details if not in its over-all structure), that it is a dynamic system. Individual stars will form, will burn for a while and then die away, or explode and scatter their matter into interstellar space as supernovae. We must try to make this idea of change a part of our picture of the Universe.

AUG. 30th 1860*	*GALAXY FORMED*	100 YEARS AGO = *20 thousand million years ago*
1935	*OUR SUN FORMED*	25 YEARS AGO = *5 thousand million years ago*
1940	*OUR EARTH FORMED*	20 YEARS AGO = *4 thousand million years ago*
1954	*FIRST FOSSILS*	6 YEARS AGO = *one thousand 2 hundred million years ago*
(AUG.) 1959	*DINOSAURS*	ONE YEAR AGO = *2 hundred million years ago*
(AUG.) 1960	*EARLY MAN*	ONE AND THREE-QUARTER DAYS AGO = *one million years ago*
AUG. 30th 1960	*MAN BUILDS AN URBAN COMMUNITY*	25 MINUTES = *8000 years ago*
AUG. 30th 1960	*CHRISTIAN ERA BEGINS*	5¼ MINUTES = *2000 years ago*
AUG. 30th 1960	*GALILEO'S FIRST TELESCOPE*	55 SECONDS = *350 years ago*
AUG. 30th 1960	*BATTLE OF TRAFALGAR*	24½ SECONDS = *155 years ago*
AUG. 30th 1960	*SECOND WORLD WAR BEGINS, 1939*	3 SECONDS = *21 years ago*
AUG. 30th 1960	*TODAY*	ZERO HOUR

* AUG. 30, 1860, WOULD IN REALITY BE 20 THOUSAND MILLION YEARS AGO.

Fig. 2.

We must try also to obtain a perspective in time, to appreciate the Earth in the temporal pattern of the Universe.

The natural unit of time to take here would be the period of the Sun around the center of the Galaxy —the cosmic year. In our imagination let us suppose that this period of 200 million years is contracted to one year (Fig. 2). The oldest stars in our Galaxy seem to be about 20,000 million (normal) years old, the Sun perhaps 5,000 million. The Galaxy, on the *speeded-up* time scale, would look like a giant Catherine wheel, the central parts whirling rapidly around, the outer regions moving at a more leisurely pace, taking many years to move around the center. The whole system would seem to be alive with a changing pattern of light. The spiral structure so obvious on a photograph of a galaxy would be seen to be an ephemeral pattern that would form and dissolve in a few days to be replaced by another spiral pattern (for the spiral arms mark out the location of bright-blue stars, whose lifetimes, on the usual time scale, are a few million years only). Every minute or so, a spot here, a spot there would flash with light—these are the supernovae, stars ending their lives in explosion. Every hour or so, we might see the appearance of puffs of bright smoke—if we look closely at such a puff, we see it as a group of stars forming out of interstellar matter, the group being spread out and disintegrated by the non-uniform rotation of our giant Catherine wheel.

Perhaps seventy-five cosmic years after the Galaxy came into existence, just such a puff of smoke could have been seen. There was nothing to distinguish it from similar puffs at a glance, but one of the stars then formed was the Sun. For the next twenty-five cosmic years, if we looked closely at the spot of light that is the Sun, it would have appeared to change very little, but a closer look would show that, during this time, the Sun had acquired a number of planets. If we were able to look even more closely at one of these planets, the Earth, we would have seen that about six cosmic years ago primitive forms of life (microscopic plant life like the scum upon a stagnant pool) had developed, and had left simple fossils in the rocks of the Earth. As we followed the fossil history, we would see life on Earth becoming ever more complex. About one cosmic year ago we would have found the Earth inhabited by giant lizards, the dinosaurs. Last (cosmic) week we would have found the saber-toothed tiger. Yesterday we would have found the Megatherium, or giant sloth; and, if he had not been too insignificant to notice, the first man. For all yesterday and most of today, Man remained a savage, but about four hours ago he learned to speak. Half an hour or so ago, he began to build cities. On the cosmic time scale, the whole process of civilization has taken less than an hour.

II. THE EARTH AS AN ABODE OF LIFE

In the first chapter I attempted to describe briefly the Universe as pictured by modern astronomers, and to emphasize that it is a *dynamic* universe. This emphasis on the dynamic nature of the Universe, and a preoccupation with processes occurring in it, are characteristic of a mature science which has graduated from the purely descriptive phase. It is our purpose to describe life as a process occurring within the physical Universe.

We are faced immediately with the difficulty that it is not possible to define the characteristics that distinguish an animate from an inanimate object in any generally accepted way. The differences between a dog and a stone are only too obvious; but it is a more difficult matter to distinguish between a very simple organism, such as a virus, and a complex but inanimate crystal. Indeed, there is no general agreement on whether a virus should be classed as a living organism or not, for life seems to shade almost imperceptibly into non-life. This problem of definition is one that will be faced, if not completely solved, in a later chapter. For the moment, we will use the word "life" to mean organisms that are, in a broad way, similar to the more highly developed living things on Earth, organisms with similar chemistry and making similar demands on their environment. With this restriction in mind, we may ask, "What characteristics of the Earth, as a planet of the Sun, are essential for the maintenance of life as we know it?"

Solar Energy

A summary of the physical and chemical nature of life must begin, not on the Earth, but in the Sun; in fact, at the Sun's very center. It is here that is to be found the source of the energy that the Sun constantly pours out into space as light and heat. This energy is liberated at the center of the Sun as billions upon billions of nuclei of hydrogen atoms collide with each other and fuse together to form nuclei of helium, and, in doing so, release some of the energy that is stored in the nuclei of atoms. The output of light and heat of the Sun requires that some 600 million tons of hydrogen be converted into helium in the Sun every second. This the Sun has been doing for several thousands of millions of years.

The nuclear energy is released at the Sun's center as high-energy gamma-radiation, a form of electromagnetic radiation like light and radio waves, only of very much shorter wavelength. This gamma-radiation is absorbed by atoms inside the Sun, to be re-emitted at slightly longer wavelengths. This radiation, in its turn, is absorbed and re-emitted. As the energy filters through the layers of the solar interior, it passes through the X-ray part of the spectrum, eventually becoming light. At this stage, it has reached what we call the solar surface, and can escape into space, without being absorbed further by solar atoms. A very small fraction of the Sun's light and heat is emitted in such directions that, after passing unhindered through interplanetary space, it hits the Earth.

It is the solar light and heat that maintain the surface of the Earth at a temperature equable for life. In fact, the temperature of the surface of a planet is closely related to the amount of solar radiation falling on each square inch of the surface. The solar radiation is absorbed by the planet, and re-emitted as long-wavelength infrared or heat waves. The planet, therefore, heats up until the energy that it radiates into space because of its temperature exactly balances the amount of energy that it absorbs from sunlight. When the Sun is overhead, the energy falling per unit area is greater than when the sunlight falls obliquely, and the tropics are, on the average, hotter than the poles. If the planet keeps the same face always to the Sun (as does Mercury), then there will be great extremes of temperature between the dark side and the sunlit side. If, on the other hand, the planet rotates rapidly, this will tend to even out the temperature between the day and night sides, as the ground will not get rid of its energy immediately it has absorbed it; there is always a lag. And one of the most important factors affecting the temperature of a planet is the presence or absence of an atmosphere.

Light takes about eight minutes to reach us from the Sun. It takes less than a thousandth of a second to pass through the Earth's atmosphere. Yet in this short time it is profoundly modified. Some of the solar radiation is completely absorbed, the energy going into heating the atmosphere. In fact, of the complete spectrum from gamma-radiation to very long radio waves, there are only two regions to which the Earth's atmosphere is transparent. One, the "optical window," covers visible light and neighboring wavelengths, while the "radio window" occurs in the radio part of the spectrum (wavelengths between a few millimeters and about 100 meters).

Greenhouse Effect

At lower levels some of the radiation may be reflected backward into space by clouds, thus reducing the temperature of the Earth's surface. But a cloudy day is not necessarily a cold day, for besides reflecting back some of the incoming solar radiation, clouds may also reflect back to Earth some of the heat radiation of the ground, thereby increasing the surface temperature.

Furthermore, with or without clouds, the atmosphere of the Earth acts like a greenhouse (Fig. 3). A greenhouse becomes warm because of a special property of glass; namely, that it is transparent to visible light but opaque to infrared radiation and heat rays.

The light of the Sun can pass through the glass, to be absorbed by the soil and structure of the greenhouse. It is then re-emitted as heat rays, which cannot pass through the glass. The amount of energy in the greenhouse thus rises, until its temperature is high enough for the slight leakage of heat rays through the glass to take away as much energy as gets in as sunlight. To a lesser extent but in a similar way, the Earth's atmosphere bottles up the energy of the Sun.

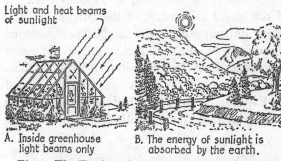

Light and heat beams of sunlight

A. Inside greenhouse light beams only

B. The energy of sunlight is absorbed by the earth.

Fig. 3. The Earth and its vegetation absorb energy from the Sun and reradiate it. In a greenhouse incoming ultraviolet radiation passes through the glass, but reradiated heat energy is trapped.

The main constituents of the atmosphere that contribute to this "greenhouse effect" are water vapor and carbon dioxide, which together amount to only one five-hundredth of a per cent of the atmosphere as a whole. Relatively small changes in the constitution of the atmosphere might have a marked effect on the terrestrial temperature. In past geological ages lush vegetation grew in Greenland, and it has been

suggested that this fact was a result of excessive vol-
canic activity that belched carbon dioxide into the
atmosphere, thus increasing the surface temperature
by increasing the efficiency of the atmospheric greenhouse. (But it may be that the pole of the Earth in
the past was not near Greenland, anyway!) Man
himself may, unwittingly, be changing the average
temperature of the Earth by sending into the atmosphere carbon dioxide from industrial chimneys. About
10 billion tons of carbon dioxide are added to the
atmosphere every year in this way, about a millionth
of the total CO_2 content of the atmosphere. The
effects are cumulative, and it may be that if industrial
expansion continues at its present rate, in the course
of a few centuries the composition of the atmosphere
will have changed enough to melt the polar caps of
the Earth, and inundate much of the land-mass of the
Earth (including London) with salt water!

Photosynthesis and Oxygen

As we have seen, when the solar radiation falls on
the ground, it is absorbed, only to be re-emitted later
as radiation of longer wavelength. If the solar radiation should fall on the leaves of a plant, however, it
is absorbed, but not re-emitted; instead, it is stored
up as chemical energy, by the process known as
photosynthesis. Using as raw materials water and carbon dioxide (obtained either from natural water or
the air), together with the energy of sunlight, a plant
can produce sugar (a typical *organic* substance), re-

leasing oxygen in the process. The reaction (much simplified) can be represented by the chemical equation:

$$6CO_2 + 6H_2O + \text{solar energy} = C_6H_{12}O_6 + 6O_2$$

The sugar molecule ($C_6H_{12}O_6$) contains the absorbed solar energy, bottled up, as it were, and ready for future use, just as the spring of a watch may be wound up ready to drive the hands. The plant can then convert the sugar into proteins and fats, which still contain the imprisoned energy.

While plants, under the influence of sunlight, can build up organic material from inorganic matter, animals (including Man) cannot. They depend, in the end, upon plant life—either eating it directly, or eating the flesh of animals that have done so. If a sudden pestilence or change of climate should destroy plant life on Earth, then all the animal life would become extinct within a few weeks. In this sense, all animals are parasites.

Thus, when an animal eats, it is, in fact, absorbing some energy derived from the Sun. This is a useful activity only if it can use this energy when it wishes to some purpose. The main chemical method of releasing the energy is by combustion, or burning with oxygen. The process is chemically the exact reverse of photosynthesis. The rates at which these chemical reactions proceed in living creatures are controlled by chemical substances which are present in very small amounts only, and which are not used up in the reactions. These substances are called enzymes, and the correct functioning and co-ordination of the complex chemical activity of living organisms depends upon the presence of these enzymes in the correct proportions.

The oxygen required for combustion is obtained by animals directly from the air, or from water in which the atmospheric oxygen is dissolved. And we here find another, more subtle way in which animal life on Earth is dependent upon plant life. Oxygen combines easily with other elements. It seems probable that not only is the present proportion of oxygen in the Earth's atmosphere maintained by the plant life on the Earth (through photosynthesis), but that the oxygen in the atmosphere may have come from plant life in the past. Life on Earth may well have developed in an atmosphere without oxygen.

It is worth remembering that nearly all the energy available on the Earth has been derived from the Sun. Consider, for example, electricity generated from hydroelectric stations. The power is obtained from water falling from a high level to a low level. But the water in the high lake is maintained only because the Sun evaporates water from the seas; the evaporated water forms clouds which can drift over the high-level lakes and deposit as rain. The steam train using coal and the automobile using gasoline are both using bottled solar energy, for coal and gasoline are the remains of vegetation that formerly flourished on the Earth by absorbing the Sun's rays. And even the energy released by my muscles, as I write on my typewriter, came, originally, from the center of the Sun.

Temperature Range of Life

It is the amount of solar radiation falling upon a planet that primarily determines the temperature of the planet's surface, and temperature is one of the most important factors that must be considered in relation to the possibility of life. Temperature is a measure of the heat of a body; heat is a form of motion of the atoms or molecules of which the body is made. From experiments on living creatures on the Earth, we learn that the range of temperature of the organism (which may differ more or less from the temperature of its surroundings) within which active life is possible is from a few degrees below the freezing-point of water up to about 140 degrees F. At higher temperatures the complex molecules on which the chemistry of life depends begin to break up, to lose essential water, and to clog the controlling action of the enzymes.

The lower limit to "active life" is less definite. While high temperatures irrevocably destroy the living organism, an excessively low temperature may put the organism into a state of suspended animation, or latent life. Although all signs of activity cease, the organism may revive if returned to an equable temperature. Trees in Siberia have withstood temperatures as low as −75 degrees F, and some bacteria have survived in latent form for several weeks in liquid oxygen at a temperature of −300 degrees F. Apparently, no lower limit can be placed upon the temperature in which *latent* life is possible. But the range of temperature for *active* life is very narrow, only

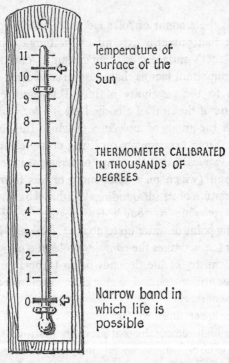

Fig. 4. The temperatures in which life can exist compose a very narrow band in the Universe's whole range of temperatures.

about 120 degrees F wide (Fig. 4). This is minute compared with the range of temperatures found in nature—from several thousand million degrees in the centers of stars to about –400 degrees F in interstellar

space. It would seem that life must exist, if at all, on a
planet, for the surface of a star is too hot and interstellar space is too cold. But it must be on a planet
which is at the right distance from a star of the right
luminosity. As we shall see in the next chapter, in the
solar system only the Earth and, to a lesser extent,
Venus and Mars present the right temperature conditions to overlap the range of active life we know. The
normal range of variation of temperature over the
Earth and with the seasons is from −75 degrees F
to +140 degrees F, which just nicely covers the
"range of active life." Indeed, is there not something
suspicious about this accuracy? It might be argued, of
course, that if life requires such stringent conditions
for its active existence, then it will appear only where
such conditions are fulfilled, even if life itself is
thereby a very rare phenomenon. But is it not equally
possible that the "range of active life" found from
observations of terrestrial life is simply a reflection of
the fact that those forms of life most fitted to the environment of the Earth have developed at the expense of those less fitted? There are on Earth some
simple bacteria, found in hot springs, that can grow at
temperatures as high as 170 degrees F, and survive
exposure of several hours to temperatures as high as
250 degrees F. Perhaps, under other conditions, these
bacterial forms would have been the basis for the
evolution of other, stranger forms of life fitted to
higher temperatures. But this is speculation. For life
as we know it on the Earth, we would seem to require a temperature confined to a narrow range, with
an atmosphere containing oxygen and some carbon

dioxide, together with the presence of free water. In the next chapter, I will have a look at some of the other planets of the solar system with these conditions in mind.

III. THE SOLAR SYSTEM

In examining the peculiar properties of the Earth, as a planet of the Sun, that seem to be necessary to sustain living creatures of the types found on the Earth, we have seen that the higher forms of life require an atmosphere containing oxygen, or else water in which oxygen has been dissolved. Plant life does not necessarily need this oxygen—indeed, the oxygen in the Earth's atmosphere may have originated from the activity of plant life at an earlier stage of the Earth's history—but does require available carbon dioxide. It is the particular property of plants that they can absorb solar energy, and store it up as chemical energy by building from carbon dioxide and water heavier, larger chemical molecules.

But by far the most important requirement of life on Earth would seem to be an equable temperature. The range of temperature that allows for *active* life is very small, from about 20 degrees F to 140 degrees F. The upper temperature limit is the more important, for if the temperature is too high, the complex molecules upon which the chemical activity of life seems to depend begin to break up. The lower limit is much less definite, for life may, at low temperatures, assume a latent form. Though not active at the low temperature, life does not die, but will recover and become active if the temperature is raised.

Measuring the Planets' Temperatures

In this chapter we look at the other planets of the solar system with these limitations in mind, and we consider first the temperature criterion. The temperature of a planet's surface depends, first, upon its distance from the source of heat and light, the Sun. If the planet had no atmosphere, and absorbed all the radiation falling upon it, then it would be easy to calculate the temperature at which the planet's surface would stabilize at any given distance from the Sun. It is important to notice that the temperature depends upon the property of the *planet*; space itself, in the solar system, can have no "temperature," only matter can. If an artificial planet were sent into the solar system, made of highly polished metal (so that it reflected all the radiation of the Sun falling on it, and absorbed none of it), then the interior of the artificial planet would remain completely cold, however near the Sun it went.

The temperature of the surface of a planet can be measured—approximately, at least—by using very sensitive detectors of heat. Such a sensitive detector is the *thermocouple* (Fig. 5). If a circuit of wire is made, one half being of one metal and the other half of another metal, and the two junctions are kept at different temperatures, then a small electric current will flow through the circuit. If this current is measured, the difference in temperature of the two junctions can be measured.

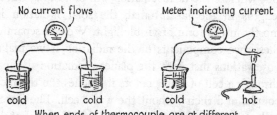

No current flows

Meter indicating current

cold   cold   cold   hot

When ends of thermocouple are at different temperatures there is a flow of current depending on the difference in temperature.

A.

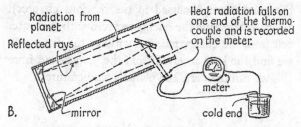

Radiation from planet

Reflected rays

Heat radiation falls on one end of the thermocouple and is recorded on the meter.

meter

B.   mirror   cold end

Fig. 5. The apparatus for measuring temperature with a thermocouple is shown in A, its application to a telescope in B.

Suppose, then, that we have such a thermocouple, and we keep one junction at the freezing point of water by immersing it in a mixture of water and ice. The other junction is placed in a telescope, so that the image of a planet falls on it. The thermocouple ab-

sorbs the energy of the heat and light from the
planet, and heats up. From the small electric current
that flows, we can tell how much energy is coming
to us from the planet (if we allow for any absorption
by the telescope itself). Now not all this energy will
be heat radiation by the planet; some of it will be
solar radiation that has been reflected by the planet.
But whereas the heat radiation will be of long wavelengths in the far infrared, the solar radiation is
mostly in the form of visible light. We can separate
these two components of the radiation if we make
observations first with the planet's radiation passing
through a cell of water before it reaches the thermocouple, and then without the water cell. The water
cell absorbs the heat rays from the planet, but is
transparent to the visible light (just like the glass of
the greenhouse discussed in the previous chapter).
So, by subtracting the energy received with the water
cell from the energy received without the water cell,
we find the heat received from the planet, and from
this we can calculate the planet's temperature.

Mercury and Venus

The planet nearest the Sun is Mercury, at a distance of 36 million miles. If we use the distance of
the Earth from the Sun (93 million miles) as our
unit of distance (the Astronomical Unit), then Mercury is nearly 0.4 Astronomical Units away from the
Sun. It keeps the same face towards the Sun, and we
would calculate its surface temperature on the sun-

ward side to be about 700 degrees F. This is close to the measured value. The dark side of Mercury is so cold that no radiation can be detected from it.

The agreement between the calculated and observed temperatures shows that Mercury has no appreciable atmosphere. We would not expect it to have. A gas consists of a large number of molecules, which, as the gas is heated up, move faster and faster, colliding with each other. When the temperature is high enough, many of the molecules acquire speeds greater than the escape speed from the planet. They then fly off into space, just as a rocket which exceeds the escape speed from the Earth's surface will become an artificial planet. In the case of Mercury, its surface temperature is so high that if it ever had any atmosphere, this would long since have evaporated into space. Any atmosphere that remains must be very, very tenuous indeed compared with the density of the Earth's atmosphere. With a temperature so far exceeding the upper limit for active life, and with no appreciable atmosphere, Mercury seems a most unlikely abode for life at all resembling life as we know it on Earth (Fig. 6).

We would expect Venus to have a temperature of about 450 degrees F at nearly three-quarters of an Astronomical Unit from the Sun. The observations give quite a different answer—about −40 degrees F. This is because Venus is covered with an extensive atmosphere, full of clouds. These clouds reflect nearly all the solar light and heat, and there is little left to heat the planet. But the same clouds will also bottle up any heat radiation from the planet, so that the actual temperature of the surface of Venus may be much higher than the observed temperature. What we are really observing is the temperature of the atmosphere of Venus above the cloud layer. In fact, this thick cloud layer prevents us from knowing

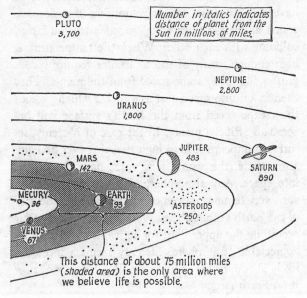

PLUTO
3,700

Number in italics indicates distance of planet from the Sun in millions of miles.

NEPTUNE
2,800

URANUS
1,800

MARS
142

JUPITER
483

SATURN
890

MECURY
36

EARTH
93

ASTEROIDS
250

VENUS
67

This distance of about 75 million miles (shaded area) is the only area where we believe life is possible.

Fig. 6. Life as we know it is possible only in a small region of the solar system.

anything about the surface conditions on Venus—we do not even know how rapidly Venus rotates, because we cannot see any permanent markings on the surface.

It is difficult also to know of what the clouds of Venus are composed. They appear very white, because they reflect so much solar radiation; this is the main reason why Venus can become the brightest object in the night sky. The method used to discover the chemical nature of the atmosphere of a planet is to look closely at the spectrum of the planet. If we pass the light of the Sun through a prism, we see a colored rainbow band with some colors missing or faint. We usually pass the light through a slit, and the missing colors appear as dark lines in the solar spectrum. There are many tens of thousands of such lines, and the particular lines that appear depend upon the chemical nature and physical conditions of the atoms in the outer layers of the Sun. If a planet simply reflected the light of the Sun, then its spectrum should be an exact replica, albeit a faint replica, of the solar spectrum. But if the planet has an atmosphere, then the sunlight has had to pass twice through the planet's atmosphere before reaching us. We might hope to see new dark lines appearing in the planet's spectrum that were *not* in the Sun's spectrum, lines produced by the atoms of the planetary atmosphere.

The spectrum of Venus has been searched for such telltale lines, in the hope of identifying the atoms of the planet's atmosphere. But such searches have been inconclusive. In particular, the characteristic groups of lines that we know to be due to water vapor do not occur in the spectrum of Venus. (This is a difficult observation, because our own atmosphere contains water vapor, and produces dark water-vapor telluric lines in both the solar and planetary spectra.) At one time it was supposed that this negative observation ruled out any possibility of the clouds' being ordinary water-vapor clouds, and many suggestions of alternative chemical constituents were made, such as solid carbon dioxide, and formaldehyde, a compound of carbon, oxygen and hydrogen. But if the temperature at the cloud level is as low as −40 degrees F, then the clouds might still be of water, but in a frozen state. If this be so, then on the surface of Venus water might exist in a free liquid state, and conditions on Venus might well be suited to the development of life. But this is just speculation. The clouds of Venus hide the secrets of the surface well, and Venus remains an enigma.

The Moon

The Earth's natural satellite, the Moon, should have an average temperature much the same as that of the Earth. But the mass of the Moon is only about an eightieth of the mass of the Earth, and so the escape velocity from the surface of the Moon is much less than that from the Earth. While the Earth has been able to retain its atmosphere over cosmic periods of time, the Moon has not. The Moon has no air, and consequently no free water lying on its surface. Also, because of aeons of tidal action by the Earth on the solid body of the Moon, the Moon keeps the same face always to the Earth (apart from a slight vestigial rotation called *libration*). Its day is, therefore, as long as a month on the Earth.

On the sunlit side of the Moon, at the middle of

the lunar day, the temperature of the surface may exceed the boiling point of water (212 degrees F). At sunset on the Moon the temperature has dropped to –50 degrees F, and at midnight on the Moon is as low as –240 degrees F (Fig. 7). Just to step across from the sunlight into the shadow of a crater or mountain on the lunar surface would be to experience a drop of

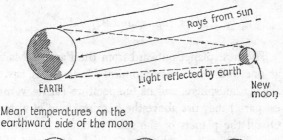

Mean temperatures on the earthward side of the moon

Lunar midday up to 220°F   Lunar sunset –50°F   Lunar midnight as low as –240 °F

Fig. 7. *Our Moon is at best an inhospitable planet, as its earthward temperatures show. Remember that water boils at 212°F!*

temperature of over 200 degrees F. Certainly the Moon seems to be no place for the development of active life. It is just possible, however, that simple organisms might be able to survive the cold of the lunar night and the heat of the lunar day in a latent form, to have a brief activity twice a month (at sunset and sunrise on the Moon). Possibly the day is not far hence when instruments may be sent to the Moon to investigate, among other matters, whether such primitive life cells do exist there. For this reason, considerable care has been taken to sterilize the attempted and successful lunar probes, so that there should be no danger of taking simple life forms to the Moon from the Earth, to contaminate it before these interesting observations could be made.

Mars, Jupiter and Beyond

The next planet outward from the Earth is Mars, at one and a half Astronomical Units. Mars has a slight atmosphere, and its temperature (at its warmest parts) may rise above the freezing point of water. Of all the planets of the solar system, Mars is the most likely one on which to find other forms of life. Furthermore, observations of Mars give some ground for believing that life of a sort does exist on Mars. For this reason, I will devote my next chapter to Mars alone.

Beyond Mars we find the giant planet Jupiter, over five times as far from the Sun as the Earth is. Its surface temperature would be expected to be around –200 degrees F, and it is covered by a most extensive atmosphere of ammonia and methane, both gases being highly poisonous to Earth-like forms of life. As we proceed outward, we come to the other giant planets, Saturn, Uranus and Neptune; these planets are even colder than Jupiter, and all have thick atmospheres of a nature similar to that of Jupiter (Fig. 8). Some of the satellites of Saturn also have

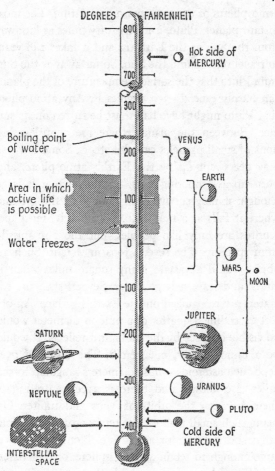

Fig. 8. The scale of our solar system temperatures.

atmospheres of the same poisonous nature. The most distant planet, Pluto, is nearly forty times as far away from the Sun as the Earth is, and it takes 248 years to travel once round the Sun. So far away is the Sun from Pluto that the surface temperature of the planet can hardly exceed −350 degrees F. Any atmosphere that Pluto might have had must be frozen on its surface. Between the planets there are countless billions of small particles called meteors. Some of these may get swept up by the Earth's atmosphere, and burn up as "shooting stars." If the meteor is large enough, it may survive partly intact to the ground, where it falls as a meteorite. Fortunately, most meteorites are only like pebbles, but the rare missile from space may be several tons in weight. Such an object would devastate many square miles when it lands, and leave a large crater. Several such meteor craters are recognized on the Earth's surface. An object exceeding a quarter of a mile in diameter would be visible in space by the sunlight it reflects. It would be a minor planet, or asteroid. The orbits of over 2000 such asteroids, whose diameters range up to 500 miles, are known, and there is a concentration of them between the orbits of Mars and Jupiter. On many such small planets, the temperature conditions might be suitable for active life. None of them is large enough to retain an atmosphere, or free water, but it is perhaps not impossible that, if the requisite chemical elements are present in the soil of the asteroid, some forms of life might arise to utilize them. If we consider that active life is possible only over the range of temperature for which life as we know it on Earth can remain active, then we see that in only a very narrow zone within the solar system—not too near the Sun, nor yet too far away—could we expect to find active life. In fact, in the distance of 3700 million miles that separates Pluto from the Sun, active life is restricted to a band only 75 million miles wide (see Fig. 6). Only the Earth, Mars and Venus, together with a few asteroids, overlap this band. Truly, in this picture of the universe life seems to be balanced precariously on a tightrope.

IV. THE PLANET MARS

If we are to find any evidence of life in the solar system outside the Earth, it is to the planet Mars that we must look. The restricted temperature range within which active life is possible limits the distance from the Sun for active life to a zone about 75 million miles wide. Within this zone lie Venus, Earth, and Mars, but Venus, as we have seen, is covered with a dense cloud layer, and conditions on the surface are almost completely unknown.

Because of its greater distance from the Sun, the surface of Mars is, on the average, colder than the Earth. An average temperature for the planet as a whole would be about -40 degrees F, compared with +59 degrees F for the Earth. But the temperature on the surface of Mars can rise above the freezing point of water. At the poles of Mars during the appropriate summer season on the planet the temperature may rise as high as +70 degrees F, but in the winter the temperature will fall to -130 degrees F. The equatorial zone on Mars suffers a much smaller variation of temperature throughout the Martian year, although here again the temperature in summer may rise a few degrees above the freezing point of water. Remembering that at temperatures below the range for active life, life may become latent, we would expect that any life forms on Mars (that do not have their own built-in temperature control such as warm-blooded terrestrial creatures have) would spend much of their time in a latent state, becoming active and self-propagating only for a brief season when the temperature is high enough.

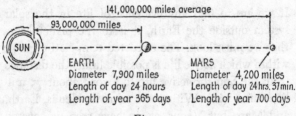

Fig. 9.

Mars takes nearly 700 of our days to move once around the Sun, and it rotates on its axis in about 24½ hours (Fig. 9). The range of temperature throughout a day on Mars is, theoretically, much the same as that on the Earth's equator, say 80 degrees F. This figure, in fact, is reached over desert regions near the Earth's equator, but in most places the daily variation is much less because of the effects of the Earth's atmosphere. The atmosphere of Mars is much thinner, and so nearly the full daily variation of temperature would be experienced there.

The Martian Atmosphere

That Mars has an atmosphere is easily seen by comparing a photograph of Mars taken in red light with one taken in blue light. The red photograph shows a number of dark markings, which are more or less permanent. A blue photograph taken at the same time will (usually) show very few markings at all. This difference arises because the Martian atmosphere scatters away the blue light of the Sun, while the red light gets through to the surface undiffused. Photographs of the Earth taken from Mars would show a similar effect.

While the differing appearances of the red and blue photographs of Mars show that it has an atmosphere, it is not possible immediately to say whether the scattering is due to the gases of the atmosphere, or to particles suspended in the atmosphere. But very occasionally it is found that the surface markings do show up on blue photographs. This rare phenomenon is called "a blue clearing." It is not at all well understood, but it does prove that most of the scattering comes from particles within the Martian atmosphere, since it is impossible that for brief periods the atmosphere as a whole should disappear. But what these particles are, and what causes their occasional absence from the Martian atmosphere, is, as yet, a mystery.

The spectrum of Mars has been examined carefully to discover the chemical nature of the Martian atmosphere. As has been discussed before, if the planet had no atmosphere, its spectrum would be a faint replica of the spectrum of the Sun, since the planet shines by reflecting sunlight. If the light from the Sun has had to pass through the planet's atmosphere, the atoms and molecules of this atmosphere may produce their own telltale absorptions. Unfortunately, the sunlight also has to pass through the Earth's atmosphere before it reaches our telescopes, and the terrestrial atmosphere produces its own absorption lines, which are much stronger than those owing to any planetary atmosphere. For this reason, it is difficult to detect in a planet's atmosphere any gases also in our own atmosphere. Extensive search has been made for evidence of water vapor in the Martian spectrum, but the search has been inconclusive just because of the heavy absorption produced by water vapor in the Earth's atmosphere. Another difficulty is that many likely gases, such as nitrogen, produce absorption lines in parts of the spectrum that are completely cut off by the Earth's atmosphere, in the ultraviolet. It may be possible, in the not too distant future, to observe the spectrum of Mars from a satellite-borne telescope above the Earth's atmosphere, when these difficulties will disappear.

However, the search of the Martian spectrum has not been without result. Positive evidence has been obtained for the presence of carbon dioxide in the Martian atmosphere. The total amount of CO_2 in the Martian atmosphere is about the same as in the Earth's atmosphere, but because the Martian atmosphere is much thinner, this corresponds to a higher percentage of CO_2, 0.2 per cent compared with 0.03 per cent for the Earth. The main constituent of the Martian atmosphere is probably nitrogen. Oxygen has not been definitely detected, and probably amounts to no more than 0.1 per cent of the atmosphere.

The total amount of atmosphere on Mars is less than a fifth of the terrestrial atmosphere, and at the planet's surface the pressure is less than a tenth of the surface pressure on Earth. But, owing to the smaller gravitational force on Mars, the density of the atmosphere drops off less rapidly with height than on the Earth. At heights above twenty miles, the atmosphere on Mars is actually more dense than the Earth's atmosphere at the same altitude. Since meteors burn up in the Earth's atmosphere at heights of about seventy miles, the thinner Martian atmosphere is actually a better protection from meteoric bombardment.

A Rusty Desert

The first thing that you would see on the surface of Mars when looking at it through a telescope would be the general orange-red color of the surface. The ruddy color of the planet, in fact, is easily noticed by the naked eye. The areas showing this red tint have been called "deserts," but it must not be supposed that the deserts on Mars are just like the deserts on Earth. Much work has gone into the study of the

spectrum of the Martian deserts. There is definite
evidence that there are some silicates present—chemical substances similar to sand. But the main constituent is probably similar to limonite, a terrestrial mineral containing a great deal of red iron oxide. Because
of the absence of oxygen in the planet's atmosphere,
it is probable that any oxygen that might have been
present has been used up in oxidizing the surface.
Mars may be a *rusty* planet!

If we were to attempt to summarize the conditions
on Mars, we would liken them to conditions in a terrestrial desert if it were transported to the poles, and
raised into the stratosphere. While certain very primitive terrestrial forms of life, such as bacteria, might
manage to survive on Mars, certainly no highly developed forms of terrestrial life could exist there without artificial aid. Yet, compared with other parts of
the universe, conditions on Mars are very similar to
those on Earth.

Seen through a telescope, the most prominent features of the Martian surface are the white polar caps.
These caps are extensive in the Martian winter, and
shrink and disappear in the Martian summer (the
summer of one hemisphere occurring at the same
time as the winter of the other). They are almost certainly composed of water, but here the similarity with
the polar snowcaps on Earth ends, for the Martian
polar caps are little more than thin layers of frost.

Blue-Green Markings

A more careful study of Mars through a telescope reveals a number of irregularly shaped dark blue-green markings (Fig. 10). They are more or less permanent—maps of Mars have been made, and the features named—but they are not exactly constant in shape or appearance. In particular, they show a variation of color with the changing seasons on Mars, in

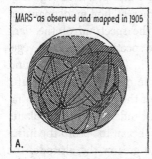
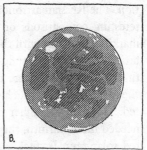

Fig. 10. The "canals" of Mars, which some astronomers can see but others can't, are mapped in A, the regional color variations in B.

time with the melting of the polar caps. There have been many hypotheses put forward to explain these markings: for example, that they are composed of minerals that change color as the moisture from the polar caps reaches them. Recently, it was suggested that, because the general pattern of the markings seemed to follow the lines that one would expect for the prevailing winds on Mars, the markings might be composed of ash from volcanoes (although no volcano has ever been observed). But in my view, the hypothesis that best explains the great variety of observations that have been made of these markings is that they are vegetation that flourishes during the short Martian summer.

One of the most cogent arguments for this view is the fact that, although we not infrequently observe dust storms in the Martian atmosphere, the dark markings are not permanently obscured by them. The markings seem to have the power of *regeneration*. The Russian astronomer Tikhoff made many interesting comparisons of the spectrum of the dark markings on Mars with the spectra of terrestrial vegetation at various altitudes in the Pamirs. He found that at low level, where the climate was temperate, the plants reflected much of the sunlight in the infrared. However at higher altitudes, where the plants needed more warmth, they began to absorb the infrared solar rays. In fact, the greater the altitude, the greater the absorption in the infrared. The spectrum of the Martian markings was very similar to the spectrum of terrestrial vegetation at the highest altitudes.

To grow and develop, plants need oxygen at considerably higher pressure than is found on Mars. But plants have a means of overcoming this deficiency. They can form oxygen in the presence of sunlight by photosynthesis, and there is no reason why this photosynthesized oxygen should not be trapped by the plant, which would build up a "local environment" with a higher oxygen content. This is just what the leaves of terrestrial plants do, and, for that matter, the lungs of human beings. The composition of the atmosphere within your lungs is rather different from the composition of the outside air.

Attempts have been made to detect in the spectrum of the dark markings on Mars the characteristic absorption lines due to chlorophyll. This crucial test

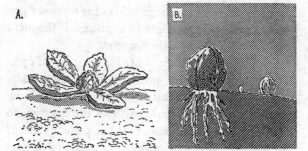

Fig. 11. *Vegetation on Mars, if it exists, must open its leaves to the Sun in daytime, store water, and close its leaves in the Martian night for protection against the cold.*

has not yet been successful, but the failure does not rule out the possibility of vegetation, since some plants on Earth, especially those in hard climates, do not show this spectrum. But although the chlorophyll spectrum has not been detected, lines that *are* found in the spectra of terrestrial plants, and that seem to be characteristic of molecules of living matter, have been detected. These lines are *not* present in the spectrum of the Martian deserts.

If we accept that the most satisfactory explanation

of the dark markings on Mars is that they are vegetation, we might speculate on the nature of such vegetation (Fig. 11). The hardiest plants on Earth are the lichens, organisms that consist of a fungus in close association with an alga. The fungus provides protection from the cold and serves as a trap for moisture. The algae build up essential organic material, and provide oxygen by photosynthesis. The fact that the general pattern of markings follows the supposed prevailing wind pattern might be explained if the plant life is propagated by spores or seeds.

Once a primitive form of life has gained hold upon a planet, we know of no limit to the complexity which life there might attain by evolution. Has intelligent life developed on Mars? This is a question to which we can give no answer at the present time. If we took our largest telescopes to Mars, and looked at the Earth, the smallest single object that we could just observe would be 100 miles across. Nothing that we could see would give any hint that intelligent life had developed on the Earth.

Martian Enigmas: "Canals" and Phobos

In the early years of this century there was much discussion about the so-called canals of Mars (see Fig. 10). Some skilled observers saw the surface of Mars covered with a network of fine, straight lines. If such a network of markings does exist, it is very difficult to think of a "natural" process that could cause them, and the suggestion that they were strips of vegetation growing along the banks of artificial canals was not unreasonable. Unfortunately, some equally skilled visual observers do not see these straight lines at all, and it is a well-known fact that the human eye tends to connect up a random set of markings at the limit of visibility with straight lines. The problem cannot be solved by photography, for, owing to the unsteadiness the Earth's atmosphere causes in the image of a planet, a photograph cannot show as fine a detail as can be seen by a trained visual observer. While some of the biggest "canals" did show up on the photographs, the existence of these broader objects is not, in any case, in dispute. But the reality of the fine network of lines remains a matter of controversy.

While a surface detail on Mars would have to be 100 miles across for it to be recognized as such, a luminous object, if sufficiently bright, could be seen, although the object is itself smaller than 100 miles. From the amount of sunlight that they reflect, we know that the satellites of Mars, Phobos and Deimos, are only a few miles in diameter (Fig. 12). Phobos, the inner one, is so near the planet's surface that it goes around Mars in a period shorter than the rotation period of Mars. From the planet it would be seen to rise in the West and set in the East, like some of our own artificial satellites. It has, in fact, been suggested seriously that Phobos might be an artificial satellite of Mars. Long series of observations have shown that Phobos has been gradually getting ahead, in its orbit, compared with its path computed under the assumption that it is moving under the attraction of Mars. Terrestrial artificial satellites speed up in just this way because of the effect of the Earth's atmosphere, which eventually causes a satellite to spiral in and fall to Earth. But if Phobos is made of rocky material, like a natural satellite, then the required

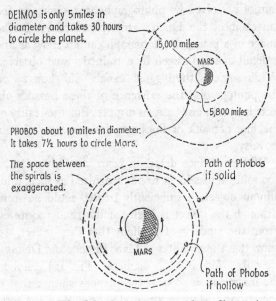

DEIMOS is only 5 miles in diameter and takes 30 hours to circle the planet.

15,000 miles

MARS

5,800 miles

PHOBOS about 10 miles in diameter. It takes 7½ hours to circle Mars.

The space between the spirals is exaggerated.

Path of Phobos if solid

MARS

Path of Phobos if hollow

Fig. 12. The Martian moons are late discoveries. Phobos's behavior is yet to be explained.

density of Martian atmosphere a few thousand miles above the planet's surface is vastly greater than is possible for the actual Martian atmosphere. For the actual atmosphere to produce the observed acceleration, the mean density of Phobos would have to be so low that it could not be other than a hollow spherical shell—a most unnatural satellite! To escape this difficulty, some astronomers have supposed that the acceleration of Phobos is due to tidal action by Mars, although this is possible only if the crust of Mars is of an entirely different composition from that of the Earth. Others have chosen the more startling hypothesis that Phobos is artificial. Only time will tell who is correct.

V. ARE THERE OTHER PLANETARY SYSTEMS?

So far we have considered the possibility that life, in a form not too dissimilar to life as we know it on Earth, might exist in our own solar system. We found that the Sun was too hot, and interstellar space too cold for active life. Only on a planet within a narrow range of distance from the Sun is the temperature suitable for active life, and within this range lie the planets Venus, Earth and Mars. Of Venus we know little, because of the extensive cloud belt that hides its surface, but in the last chapter I presented some evidence strongly supporting the view that at least vegetation exists on Mars.

While still confining our attention to life essentially similar to terrestrial life, we can ask whether there exist in space other planets, moving about other stars, that might serve as homes for living creatures. Or is the solar system an example of a very rare, if not unique, arrangement of matter in the Universe? It would be easy to answer this question if we could simply look at the nearby stars with our telescopes, and see whether they had planets; but this is not possible. Certainly a planet the size of Jupiter circling about the nearest star would reflect enough light for it to be photographed with a large telescope. But its parent star would be so much brighter that the faint image of the planet would be lost in the "glare." So, in order to find out whether planetary systems are common or not, we must turn to theories of the origin of the solar system.

Origin of the Solar System

Such theories are based upon the application of known laws of physics and attempt to explain as many of the observed properties of the solar system as possible, as arising directly from the mechanism of formation that is postulated. All such theories have to be deductive—that is to say, they start off with an idea of how the solar system began, and work through the consequences of the known laws of physics to show that a system something like the observed solar system would have been formed. It has not proved possible to work backward from the observed solar system to conditions at its formation. What seem to be suitable starting points for a theory will depend, therefore, upon the particular astronomer's view of the nature of the Universe as a whole. Another problem resides in the fact that the theory must use "known" laws of physics, for important physical processes may occur in the formation of a planetary system about which laboratory physics yet has had no indication. Thus, when Laplace put forward the famous nebular theory in the 18th century, the only forces he had to consider were gravitational. But now we know that the so-called electromagnetic forces that influence the motions of charged particles of matter cannot be ignored, although these forces were quite unknown in Laplace's day. For this reason, no theory of the origin of the solar system can be entirely conclusive.

By far the greatest difficulty arises because we do not know whether planetary systems are common or not. If the Sun, but a single star among some 100,000 million stars in our own Galaxy alone, is very unusual in having planets, then the process of formation must be one that occurs very infrequently. However, the improbability of any given theory of the origin of the solar system is not a valid objection to it.

Indeed, it is just remotely possible that the Sun picked up the planets and their satellites, one by one, by pure chance. This would be a *very improbable* theory, because the solar system shows a great many regularities. For example, all the planets move around the Sun in the same direction, and most of the satellites move around their primaries in the same direction; there is a "one-way-street" sign in the solar system. Also, most of the planets rotate about their axes in the same direction. The orbits of the planets are inclined at only small angles to each other—the solar system almost can be drawn on a flat sheet of paper. Finally, the planets (but not the minor planets or comets) move in almost circular orbits, while highly elliptical orbits (like that of Halley's Comet) are perfectly possible orbits under the Sun's gravitational pull. None of these regularities would be in any way expected if the Sun had picked up its planets by accident. It is true that some of these regularities might have arisen because of the attraction of one planet upon another, for we cannot work out what will happen, under Newton's Laws of Gravitation, to a system containing several planets (for more than a few hundred years, at least). But no astronomer has seriously adopted the "chance" hypothesis—it leads to no useful conclusion.

I do not propose to discuss, in this book, the various theories of the origin of the solar system that have been proposed from time to time, but I would like to discuss some general features of the theories. They fall into two broad categories. Some, like the original Laplace theory, see the formation of planets as an integral process in the formation of a star. If this theory were true, every star would have its planetary system. Such a theory may be called a "general" theory. On the other hand, a theory such as the tidal theory, which depends upon the close approach of two or more stars, is a very unlikely theory, demanding very special circumstances for it to operate. We may call such a theory a "particular" theory. It has been estimated that if the tidal theory were correct, only about one star in a million would have planets. (This would still give 100,000 planetary systems in our Galaxy alone, and there are several hundred million galaxies within range of the 200-inch telescope.) Some theories see the solar system as arising when the Sun passed through an interstellar cloud of matter. These are still particular theories, but the conditions required are not as stringent as those for the tidal theories—perhaps one star in a hundred would have planets.

Evidence of Other Planets

We believe that stars condense out of interstellar matter, and because of the internal motions of interstellar matter that we observe, we would expect that a "proto-star" (that is, a star in its earliest stages of condensation) would possess quite a lot of *angular momentum* (a particle of mass m moving in a circle of radius r with speed v has angular momentum $= m \times v \times r$). Now our known laws of physics tell us that, during the condensation, the star should keep this angular momentum constant, so that, as it decreases its radius (r), its speed of rotation (v) must increase; the star should rotate faster and faster. The problem is, why is the Sun not rotating much more quickly than it is? One answer is to suppose that although we do not fully understand the mechanism, a contracting star can shed some of its angular momentum by forming planets.

Now we can observe the rotations of stars, and we find that most of the hot blue stars (the young stars) are indeed rotating rapidly, but that the cool red stars of masses like the Sun (or smaller) have very little rotation. In my view, the evidence points (though not conclusively) to the view that when a star of the same size as the Sun or smaller condenses out of interstellar matter, it automatically passes through a stage where it forms planets. If this is so, then planetary systems should be very common in space.

Can we confirm this by any type of observation at all? I have said that we cannot observe a planet directly in the telescope; but there is another way whereby we might detect a planet. If we have two stars close together in space, one star will move about the other in an orbit, just as a planet moves about the Sun. We can observe this motion in the case of nearby double stars, and plot the path of one of the pair about the other. Now if the two stars are not affected by any other body, the relative orbit should appear, from the Earth, to be an ellipse. But if one of the stars has a planet, then the attraction of the third body in the system will complicate the motion; the relative orbit is no longer a perfect ellipse, but rather an ellipse with a small oscillation put on it. From the size of this oscillation, we can estimate the mass of the invisible third body. The invisible body might turn out to be a star, although one too faint to be seen directly. But in a number of cases, it turns out that the invisible companion has a mass about ten times that of Jupiter. While such mass is, by solar-system standards, heavy for a planet, it is much too small for a star. The observations that have to be made are very delicate: The deviations from the true ellipse may amount to no more than a twentieth of a second of arc or a pinhead seen from a distance of about seven miles, and we could detect such planetary bodies only if they are rather heavy (as solar-system planets go), and move around a star that is a member of a double-star system very near to the Sun. But the fact that a number of such planetary bodies have been detected in nearby double-star systems would indicate that, unless our own region of the Galaxy is particularly "planet-prone," planetary systems must be rather common. On this basis, at least one star in ten would seem to have planets. It must be remembered that, at the moment, we can observe such extrasolar planets only if they occur in double-star systems; the detection of a planet about a single star is very much more difficult.

To us, life on a planet moving about one star of a binary-star system would be very strange, for the regular succession of day and night would be disturbed, even if the planet rotated on its axis quite regularly. When the planet was on the far side of its own star, away from the companion, normal day and night would occur. But half of the planet's year later, the other star would be on the "night side" of the planet, and there would be no night, for as one "sun" set in the planet's sky, the other "sun" would rise. Life on Earth, especially the most primitive forms, is strongly regulated by the succession of day and night, and any life that might develop on the planet of a binary star would have a difficult task adjusting itself to the more varied conditions of light and darkness.

The double nature of the star system might actually make it impossible for active life (as we know it) to exist at all; there might be no part of the system that would always remain within the range of temperature required for active life. For example, if the

Sun had a companion star exactly like it, and this companion were less than twice as far as Venus away from the Sun, there would be no possible circular orbit about the Sun that was always within the temperature range for active life. (But in any case, in a double-star system like this, the orbit of a planet would be very complicated, nothing like the approximately circular orbits of the real solar system.)

Temperature and Age of Planets

The position of the zone of active life would depend upon the brightness of the parent star. If the Sun were replaced by a hot blue star with an output of light and heat some 17,000 times that of the Sun (such a star is not exceptional in space), then the

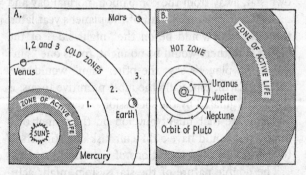

Fig. 13. *If solar radiation were reduced to one-sixteenth of its present level, life could exist (A) only within Mercury's orbit. If it were increased by a factor of 17,000 (B) life would be impossible in the solar system.*

zone of active life would stretch from two and a half times the distance of Pluto up to fifty times the distance of Pluto (Fig. 13). On the other hand, if the Sun were replaced by a cool red star with an output of heat and light only a sixteenth of the Sun's, then the zone of active life would lie wholly inside the orbit of Mercury.

If the Sun were to vary its output of heat and light, then the zone of active life would change its position in the solar system during the cycle of variation of the Sun. In fact, if the Sun changed its brightness by a factor as big as four and a half, then the zone of active life at minimum brightness would nowhere overlap the zone for maximum brightness. We do see, in space, stars whose brightness changes regularly by more than this factor. Some stars can double their brightness in less than an hour. If such a star had a planet, then life on that planet would have to remain latent during the minimum of the star's cycle, only becoming active as the star heated up and brought the planet into the zone of active life. We see, therefore, that although a high proportion of stars might have planets, the requirements for a planet suitable to life (more or less as we know it) are rather stringent. Even if the right physical conditions exist on such a planet now, there is another aspect to consider.

Life has taken over a thousand million years to evolve to its present state on the Earth. If we suppose that this is typical for the evolution of life of about the same degree of intelligence as Man, then, even among those planets for which the temperature conditions are right, we would have to select only those planets whose ages (and so the ages of their parent stars) were several thousand million years. Many stars are much younger. When the factors we have discussed are taken into consideration, it is found that of the forty stars nearest to the Sun only two satisfy the necessary conditions for the possible evolution of intelligent life more or less similar to Man. Of course, there are a great many uncertainties in such a calculation, but it does give some idea of the possible frequency with which we could expect to find intelligent life on planets about other stars. This calculation was made by an American astronomer with a quite serious purpose, for attempts are being made to see if evidence for the existence of intelligent life outside the solar system can be obtained. They depend upon using radio telescopes. Such telescopes pick up, not light or heat from space, but radio waves. The Universe itself emits quite a lot of radio radiation, but this is of the nature of "random noise" —that is to say, if the radio signal is put through a loudspeaker, a hiss results. An artificial radio transmission with a meaningful signal will be quite different from random noise in pattern. At the new United States National Radio Observatory, in West Virginia, a systematic search for such "intelligent signals" in the radio waves from space has begun. Lest this discussion would seem to be like science fiction, I must emphasize that the search for such signs of "intelligence" is being undertaken in all seriousness. It is impossible to estimate the chance of its succeeding—or even the probability of recognizing intelligent radio signals if they are observed—but if such a project did succeed, it could not do other than profoundly affect our attitude to life and the Universe.

VI. WHAT IS LIFE?

So far, I have been considering "Life and the Universe" on the assumption that by the word "life" is meant any type of organism with the same (or closely similar) physical and chemical make-up as living things on Earth; it has been assumed that the range of conditions for active life that is found for earthly creatures can be applied outside the Earth. It is, of course, possible that this is true, that any form of activity that could be called "life" in a wider sense can occur only within the narrow range of conditions found on the Earth and its neighboring planets. But it is equally possible that the life forms that we find on Earth are just those that have evolved and developed because they are suited to earthly conditions; forms that have remained primitive on Earth might, in the conditions on a different planet, have evolved and developed.

In the face of this difficulty, writers seem to have taken up two attitudes. One is that since we know of no limit to the power of evolution to produce the most diverse forms of life, life is possible almost anywhere in the Universe, except perhaps inside a star! The other attitude is to say that, since we know of life only as it occurs on Earth, it is merely speculative to talk of other forms of life; we will resolutely call any planet upon which earthly life could not exist "lifeless."

I believe that both attitudes are wrong, that both are, in fact, equally "speculative." The middle course is to be prepared to recognize that there may well be limits to the physical conditions in which any form of life is possible (and try to learn something about these limits by considering the fundamental nature of the living process) but not to adopt the medieval attitude that the Earth is the measure of the Universe. In other words, we must be prepared to speculate, but our speculation must be controlled as far as possible by knowledge.

Is There a Life Force?

At once we are faced with the difficulty of trying to discover what it is that distinguishes living organisms from non-living ones. Two views have been held about this. The mechanistic view is that, in principle, the whole of the properties of what we call living creatures could be explained (if we knew enough about them) in terms of physics and chemistry. In this view, there is no sharp dividing line between living and non-living matter, and the one grades imperceptibly into the other. The alternative view is the vitalistic one, that living matter is different *in kind* from non-living matter, being activated by some vital force that is outside the realms of physics and chemistry.

We are a long way from explaining all the properties of life in terms of everyday science, and while any gaps remain, it is possible for the vitalistic view to be held. But it is interesting to take some of the properties of living matter that vitalists have supposed to support their views, and see how far the same properties are shared by some non-living systems. As an astronomer, I naturally turn to stars as non-living comparisons, but others are possible. I must emphasize that I am in no way suggesting that stars are somehow "living"—it is precisely because I am sure that the word "living" is not applicable to a star that the comparisons serve to show just how difficult it is to define what we mean by "life" in any fundamental sense.

To make this comparison, we must first understand how the matter in a star is organized—how a star works.* To lift a pencil off my desk, I have to use some energy, and this energy is preserved as "potential energy" which the pencil has by virtue of its position. If I now let the pencil go, the gravitational pull of the Earth causes the pencil to fall, and in doing so to acquire a velocity. The potential energy of the pencil is converted into kinetic energy, or energy of motion. Now a star begins as a giant condensation in

---

* For a more detailed description, see Hermann Bondi, *The Universe at Large* (Science Study Series), Doubleday, 1960.

interstellar matter. Each part of the star exerts a gravitational pull on every other part, and the star begins to contract. As it does so, its potential energy is converted into energy of motion of the atoms of which the star is composed, and this kinetic energy is what we call heat. So the star gets hot. When the center of the star has reached the right temperature (about 15 million degrees C), nuclear reactions begin to generate energy, and the star's contraction halts. The star is then in balance, for at every point inside the star the weight of the star's material lying above it is just balanced by the pressure of the gas of which the star is made. Since the weight of overlying material increases as we go into the star, so the pressure must increase as we go inward. But the pressure of a gas increases as its temperature increases, so the temperature must also increase as we go inward.

It has been said that a living organism is different from a non-living body because "the whole is greater than the parts of which it is made." Even if the behavior of an individual cell of a living organism were understood, this would not mean that we could explain the organism as a whole—for example, a living cell cannot live if removed from the body of which it was a part. But a bit of a star cannot shine by itself, for if we took a piece of a star away, it would immediately evaporate into space and grow cold. The generation of energy inside a star depends upon there being the weight of the whole star outside the center. One part of the star interacts with another part. If we took a bit of matter from the center of a star and applied to it the same forces that it was subjected to inside the star, then it would shine; and, in the same way, a cell can be made to live and grow outside its original body if it is put in the right "culture medium," this medium imitating for the cell the conditions that the cell found in the living organism. In fact, the "whole being greater than the parts" is a commonplace of physics; in any physical system we have to consider both the nature of the parts and the interactions between them. In this sense, a watch is more than the sum of the cogs, springs and wheels of which it is made.

Or again, it has been suggested that the ability to heal itself after injury is a peculiar property of a living organism. But what would happen to a star if we removed a part of it? It immediately would resume its original spherical shape, and be a perfectly good star, albeit not as heavy as it was originally. The star would have "healed" itself. The reason that it does this is that the removal of part of the star destroyed the symmetry of internal forces in the star; those parts of the star at the edge of the cut were pushed (by the pressure of the stellar material) *from one side only*, so they moved until the pressure on both sides balanced. Something very similar, although rather more complicated, and more in the realms of chemistry than physics, is true of the cells of my finger when I cut it, and this asymmetry of conditions leads to the organism's adjusting itself to a new symmetrical condition—i.e., healing itself.

Living things have been supposed to be characterized by being able to react to unforeseen circumstances. Yet is this not also true of the star in my hypothetical experiment? The star certainly was not formed with that particular experiment in mind.

Stars as "Organisms"

Surely the ability to reproduce itself is peculiar to a living organism? But it must be remembered that an organism must obtain material from its surroundings in order to reproduce, and we can imagine a set of circumstances (unlikely in nature, it is true, but not impossible) whereby a star might reproduce itself. Suppose we begin with a rapidly rotating star, which is still in the process of contraction. As it contracts, the star will rotate more and more rapidly (see the previous chapter), and, if the original rotation is rapid enough, it may break up into two smaller stars. If the double star that it has now become should then move into a cloud of interstellar matter, the gravitational pull of the stars would attract some of the interstellar matter. The stars would then grow by *accretion*, and could grow into two stars as large as the original single star, the extra material being provided from outside the original star.

Living things learn from experience; that is to say, their reaction to a given set of circumstances depends upon what has happened to them in the past. It would doubtless be possible to construct some highly artificial circumstances in which this would be true of a star, but a simpler example is available. The more frequently a metal bar is bent and straightened again, the easier it is to bend it next time. The process of bending the bar changes its physical nature, so that it is no longer the same bar; but, likewise, an organism that has had a particular experience is no longer the same organism as it was before. With present technology, it would be perfectly possible to build a calculating machine that not only could play a passable game of chess, but also could learn from its mistakes to improve its game!

Another property of living organisms is that they seem to be arranged in different levels as regards their functions. The activity of certain parts of my body is controlled by chemicals called hormones in my blood, the presence of which is controlled by my glands, which in turn are controlled (albeit unconsciously) by my brain. But we find a similar *hierarchy of function* in the Universe; the motion of a moon is controlled by a planet, and planets' motions are controlled by stars, whose motions are controlled by the gravitational pull of the Galaxy (and possibly the motions of galaxies are controlled by the gravitational pull of a supergalaxy).

Doubtless such examples could be multiplied, but enough has been said to cast strong doubts on the view that living things are in some ways different *in kind* (and not merely in complexity) from non-living things. Rather is it more likely that the division between the living and the non-living is not sharp, but that the simplest living things differ only imperceptibly from complex non-living things. Indeed, the virus particles (which I shall mention in the next chapter) seem to be like complicated chemical crystals which have some, but not all, properties of life.

The interesting possibility then arises that living things might be able to evolve naturally from non-living things. I will discuss this possibility in Chapter VIII.

Ability to Resist Decay

Yet, when all this has been said, there still remains the feeling that living things, as we find them on Earth, are somehow different from earthly non-living things. Part of this feeling is no doubt associated with the idea of *consciousness*. Consciousness is a very difficult idea to deal with scientifically, for while we have direct experience of our *own* consciousness, we can experience consciousness in other creatures only if we have some means of communication with them. In any case, it is doubtful that it can be said that the simplest undoubtedly living organisms have consciousness at all, so it is probably not a quality that distinguishes life from non-life. But there is more to the feeling of difference than this. I think it is that living things seem to have the ability to resist decay.

Non-living things seem always to tend to change from the more highly arranged state to the less highly arranged. A house of cards will fall down by itself, but if you throw a pack of cards into the air, you would be surprised if it fell down as a house of cards! On the other hand, the pattern or *structure* of a living thing seems to remain, even though the material of which the living thing is made changes. With the important exception of his brain, the matter of which a human being is made is being constantly replaced, yet he remains recognizably the same human being. It is true that in the higher forms of life individuals must die; but part of the pattern or structure which makes a Man recognizably himself lives on in his children. This is more clearly shown in a simple, single-celled creature such as the amoeba, a microscopic form which lives in pond water. An amoeba reproduces itself simply by dividing into two smaller amoebae, which then grow to full size exactly like the original one. While an amoeba may be killed by adverse circumstances, given the right environment, the amoeba is, in a real sense, "eternal." As an analogy to this property of living things, I have in mind a whirlpool. Water flows into one side of the whirlpool, and out of the other; yet the pattern of the whirlpool remains. Of course, the comparison is only superficial, for the structure of the whirlpool is maintained by forces outside it—the play of wind on water, and the distribution of rock—while a living thing has within its own make-up this ability to keep its structure while the material of which it is made changes.

VII. MOLECULES AND LIFE

In the last chapter, I attempted to discover what, if anything, fundamentally distinguished living matter from non-living matter. I did this by comparing some features of the behavior of living matter—self-healing, self-reproduction, etc.—which might have been supposed to be peculiarly behavior of living matter, with the behavior of a star under certain (hypothetical) experiments. The suggestion was made that there was no sharp dividing line between living matter and non-living matter. Nevertheless, the feeling that living things on Earth are somehow different from non-living things must reflect some real difference of behavior, and I suggested that this might be that living things seem to have, within themselves, the ability to resist decay.

At first sight, this hypothesis seems to be the exact opposite of everyday experience. Have not the stones of Stonehenge stood through a hundred generations of men? But let us look a little closer. Although individual living things may die, the pattern or structure of matter that makes them peculiarly themselves lives on in their offspring, so that it is with life itself, and not with individual living things, that the stones of Stonehenge must be compared. Also, Stonehenge is not *active*. If Stonehenge does anything at all, it will be to fall down, to destroy its present structure. It is the ability to retain its structure while, nevertheless, indulging in activity that seems to distinguish living from non-living things on Earth.

Order and Disorder

One of the triumphs of classical physics was to show that this tendency to decay (which is technically known as *the second law of thermodynamics*) is a consequence of pure chance. We can define "decay" more precisely as "a decrease in the order of the system." The word "order" here has a precise scientific significance, but it does correspond closely to the ordinary ideas of order. For example, a set of billiard balls in the triangular rack at the start of a game of pool is a more ordered arrangement than when they are scattered over the table; and so on.

To see how pure chance can lead to the destruction of order, I will consider a very simple experiment. Into a rectangular tank of water I imagine introducing at one end some red ink. This red ink consists of an enormously large number of individual particles, or molecules, of red ink, each moving, colliding with other molecules, and bouncing off. The red ink will gradually diffuse through the tank, until the water is a uniform pink color. Yet each molecule of red ink is just as likely to move one way as the other. At the boundary between the red ink and the clear water half the molecules on the left-hand side will be moving to the right and half to the left, and similarly for the molecules on the right of the boundary. But, because there are *more* ink molecules on the side where the ink was introduced than on the other, more molecules will be moving into the clear water than will be moving from the clear water into the ink. And so, the boundary moves through the water until the ink is uniformly distributed throughout the water. Pure chance in the behavior of each individual molecule has produced a regular behavior in a large number of molecules.

We would say that the state when all the red ink was in one half of the tank was a more ordered state than when the ink was diffused throughout the tank. Heat (i.e., the random motion of the molecules of a gas or a body) is another form of disorder.

Now a living organism is obviously a very highly ordered system, and when it is indulging in activity, it must decrease its order (this decrease in order often appearing as heat). It can retain its highly ordered pattern only by absorbing *order* from its surroundings. With animals it is not difficult to realize that when they eat *other* living things (animals or plants), they are absorbing matter in an ordered form. Plants have the ability to use the energy of the Sun to produce order; by photosynthesis they produce complicated, highly ordered molecules of substances such as

sugar ($C_6H_{12}O_6$) from simpler, less highly ordered
molecules such as carbon dioxide (CO_2) (Fig. 14).
In a sugar solution the twenty-four atoms that go to
make up the sugar molecule remain together and
move together, whereas in a solution of carbon dioxide, the unit is a molecule with only three atoms;

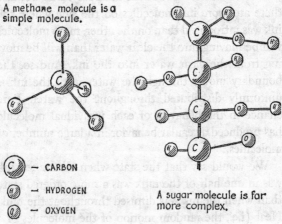

A methane molecule is a
simple molecule.

A sugar molecule is far
more complex.

(C) — CARBON
(H) — HYDROGEN
(O) — OXYGEN

*Fig. 14. Methane (marsh gas) and sugar are com-
posed of the same elements, but their molecular
structures differ greatly in complexity.*

a sugar solution is a more highly ordered arrangement
of matter than a solution of carbon dioxide, in exactly the same way that an eightsome reel is a more
highly ordered dance than the waltz.

But we have shifted the problem only one stage
further, for we now have to ask why the order of a
complex molecule (such as the sugar molecule) does
not spontaneously go over into disorder, the molecule
spontaneously breaking up into smaller units.

Building of Cells

Perhaps the greatest discovery of physics in the 20th century so far is that the classical laws of physics (such as the second law of thermodynamics), while true for large collections of atoms or molecules, do *not* apply to single atoms or molecules. The right laws in these cases are very different, and together form what is called the *quantum theory*. Put at its simplest, the quantum theory says that the state of a *single* atom or a *single* molecule can change only by discrete jumps; the atom cannot slide continuously from one state to another. We may think of the difference between the two types of law as the difference between a steep slope and a flight of stairs, "top" being a state of order and "bottom" being a state of disorder. If classical laws were true of a single molecule at the top of the slope, it simply would slide steadily into disorder. But the quantum laws say that the molecule is at the top of a flight of stairs. It will stay there unless it is pushed. If it is pushed, it can drop onto a lower stair, and still stay there. Therefore, a molecule will not decay spontaneously, but only if it absorbs some definite amount of disorder from outside. A living organism is obviously a collection of a very large number of molecules; yet in a strange way it seems to share this property of a *single* molecule.

One of the most fascinating and exciting stories of modern science is the way in which biophysics has been showing that a living organism does actually depend upon the properties of a very few individual, submicroscopic molecules.

A living body is made up of microscopic cells. A simple organism, such as an amoeba, may consist of only one cell, whereas a more advanced organism may contain an enormous number of cells. (For example, a cubic centimeter of human liver tissue contains about 200 million cells.) Each cell has a central body, the nucleus (Fig. 15). Around the nucleus is a semi-fluid region, the cytoplasm, which is itself enclosed

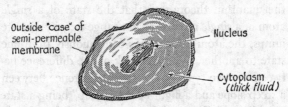

Outside "case" of
semi-permeable
membrane

Nucleus

Cytoplasm
(thick fluid)

Fig. 15. The general structure of cells.

by a surrounding wall, which may or may not be rigid. The correct functioning of these cells in their respective places in the living organism is related to certain chemical substances called proteins which are found in the cytoplasm. A protein molecule consists of one or more strings of carbon atoms. To each carbon atom is attached a particular group of atoms forming a definite structure. Each one of these groups is characteristic of a particular amino acid; a protein molecule consists of one or more strings of amino acids. The chemical behavior of the particular protein molecule depends not only upon which amino acids it contains, but also *the order in which they are strung along the chain.* The action of each protein is highly specific. Hemoglobin in human blood contains protein molecules that have many thousands of amino-acid groups (of nineteen different types), and it is well known from experience in blood transfusion that blood of one group will not necessarily serve as a substitute for blood of another. The differences between the groups reside in the order in which the amino acids are built into the proteins.

A cell has to manufacture new protein continually, and the protein must be exactly the right type, having its amino-acid units in exactly the right order. The control of this process seems to reside in the cell nucleus, in certain acids (nucleic acids) that are found there. A molecule of nucleic acid is also a long chain of carbon atoms with special groups of atoms attached; this time there are only four different units, called adenine—which I will represent by (A)—guanine (G), cytosine (C) and thymine (T). Again, it is the order in which the special groups (or nucleotides) are strung along the nucleic-acid chain that is all-important. If a particular sequence of nucleotides occurs at a part of the nucleic-acid molecule, then a particular amino acid (and that particular one only) can, so to speak, stick to the nucleic-acid molecule. As the various amino acids come to the nucleic-acid molecule, it will either accept them (if there is a vacant space for them) or reject them. When the whole chain has been filled up, the amino acids can join together and strip off the nucleic-acid molecule as a protein molecule (Fig. 16). In other words, the

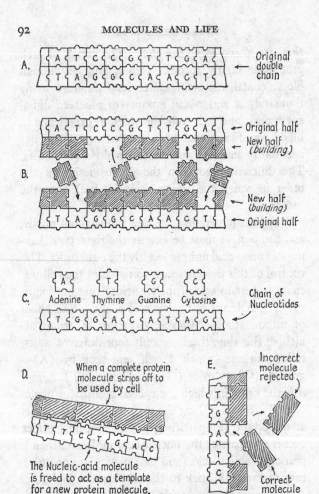

A. → Original double chain

B. → Original half
→ New half (building)
→ New half (building)
→ Original half

C. Adenine Thymine Guanine Cytosine → Chain of Nucleotides

D. When a complete protein molecule strips off to be used by cell

The Nucleic-acid molecule is freed to act as a template for a new protein molecule.

E. Incorrect molecule rejected
Correct molecule

Fig. 16. The formation and reproduction processes of the two building blocks of living cells, nucleic acid and amino acid, are illustrated in this sequence.

nucleic-acid molecule acts as a *template* on which the protein molecules are built, and the pattern of the template determines the pattern of the resulting protein molecule.

The Template of Life

The nucleic acid that serves as a template for protein molecules is found both in the cell nucleus and in the cytoplasm where the protein is manufactured. But there is another type of nucleic acid that is found in the nucleus only. It is made of the same nucleotides, and seems to serve as a template for the manufacture of the first nucleic acid. But this new nucleic acid seems to have the property of *reproducing itself*, in a similar way. When a cell divides into two cells, the material of the nucleus is divided between the daughter cells, and the new cells can function as factories of proteins of exactly the same types as those produced by the parent cell.

Modern studies of the structure of complex molecules have given us some clue to the mechanism of this important property of self-replication. The nucleic-acid molecule is in the form of two parallel chains, connected by bridges (like a stepladder). The bridges are formed by linking between a nucleotide of one chain and a nucleotide of the other. But adenine will join together *only* with thymine, and guanine will join together *only* with cytosine. If the ladder is now broken down the middle wherever A appears, it will be able to pick up only T; wherever T

appears it will be able to pick up only A, and similarly
with G and C. Thus the "left-hand" side of the ladder
will build up next to it a new "right-hand" side, and
the "right-hand" side will build up a new "left-hand"
side, and there will be two nucleic-acid molecules
where previously there was only one, and the order
of the nucleotides of the new molecules will be iden-
tical with the order in the original one.

We can see this process happening when we intro-
duce the *wrong* nucleic acid into a living cell. Certain
bacteria can be attacked by viruses. The virus particle
is too small to be seen with an ordinary microscope,
but it can be seen with the more powerful electron
microscope. It consists, essentially, of a single molecule of nucleic acid in a protective cover. It cannot
live by itself, for it has no means of making its own
chemical structures out of raw material. But inside
the bacterium the nucleic acid of the virus particle
acts as a template upon which the chemical units
manufactured by the bacterium can stick. The virus
particle thus reproduces itself at the expense of the
bacterium, which it eventually kills.

The structure of a living organism is, therefore, in a
real sense a reflection of the structure of the nucleic-
acid molecules in the nuclei of its cells, for this is what
is passed on from one generation of cells to the next.
The nucleic-acid molecule prescribes, in a chemical
"code," the nature of the living creature, and it is this
prescription that the creature passes on to its offspring. But the pattern of nucleotides in the nucleic-
acid molecule has to prescribe not only how one type
of organism differs from another type, or how one or-

ganism differs from another of the same type, but also how the various physical and chemical processes that combine in the activity of an individual are organized and properly co-ordinated. At first sight, it would seem impossible that it could do this with only four basic units. But a nucleic-acid molecule may be up to 20,000 units long. This gives the number of different possibilities as a number with about 12,000 noughts following it. Of course, not all these combinations may represent possible living creatures; but the total number of individual atoms in the whole visible Universe is a number with fewer than 80 noughts following it. So, of all the possible variations of structure of a nucleic-acid molecule built on the pattern of those that we know, only a minute fraction have ever been realized, or are ever likely to be. The nucleic-acid molecule which carries the prescription of the nature of a living creature in its chemical "code" is large by the standards of normal molecules, but by the standards of everyday life it is minute.

Suppose that from every single human being living today we took the nucleic-acid molecules from just one cell. Together, these molecules would prescribe in detail the whole human race as it exists at the present time—every man, woman and child. Yet the whole of this gigantic "card-index" would not fill an ordinary thimble! Essentially, then, the complexity of a living creature, and the endurance of its pattern, can be traced to the structure of its fundamental molecule. Now it is a significant fact that, of all the chemical elements, only carbon has the ability to form very long-chain molecules of this sort. So we can be sure of one thing at least—wherever life may appear in the Universe, its chemistry will be based on carbon. And we have come to this conclusion, not merely by saying that "all life on Earth is based on carbon," but by studying the very nature of life itself.

VIII. THE EVOLUTION OF
LIFE ON EARTH

How did life begin upon the Earth? To this question a number of suggested answers have been given from time to time. For example, it has been suggested that life might have been brought, in a primitive form, to the Earth from elsewhere in the Universe on meteorites. Now it is not inconceivable that life developing in one part of the Universe might be propagated in some such way to other parts. But this is not a fruitful suggestion, for it simply takes the question of the origin of life out of the realm of further discussion. Rather is it better to ask whether, if we accept the view that there is no sharp dividing line between living and non-living matter, we can come to understand the conditions that would be required for living matter to be built up from non-living matter on the Earth.

Even the simplest of molecules that could serve as a basis for life is a highly ordered structure of atoms, which is very unlikely to form by chance in a collection of free atoms. On the other hand, if some sticky material were available, free atoms might stick to this material, which would form a sort of matrix on which, given time, more complicated molecules could build up. Many molecules of various degrees of complexity would form in this way, only to break up again. But if, at any time, a molecule sufficiently complex, and of the right type to act as a template upon which a molecule like itself could be built (similar, but on a simpler level, to the nucleic-acid molecules discussed in the last chapter), then a train of evolution towards more complex, "living" molecules might begin.

"Proto-Life"

It has been suggested that, at an early stage in the history of the Earth's crust, the right conditions were provided on wet, muddy banks of clay that would form in the estuaries of rivers. Another suggestion has pushed the origin of "proto-life" to an even earlier period, before the Earth was formed. Some theories have supposed that the Earth (and the other planets) were built up from smaller particles, or planetesimals, by accretion (and not formed "hot" from material from the Sun). Such accretion would be facilitated where the preplanetary material was of a sticky nature, and complex molecules might have been formed on the planetesimals.

Another suggestion is that complex molecules might be built up, in the right circumstances, by the action of radiation from the Sun. The presence of the oxygen in the Earth's atmosphere shields the surface

of the Earth from the most active ultraviolet radiation of the Sun. But this oxygen has been produced
by the action of living things on Earth. The primitive
atmosphere of the Earth probably resembled more
the atmosphere of Jupiter, containing such gases as
ammonia and methane. Recently, the experiment has
been made of passing an electrical discharge through
a mixture of gases of this type, and including water,
and it has been found that in this way molecules of
amino acids can be formed. These are not yet living
molecules, but they are the bricks out of which living
molecules are built (see Chapter VII).

We may suppose, at least tentatively, that in some
such way the first self-reproducing molecules were
formed in the primitive atmosphere of the Earth. At
the same time, other complicated molecules that had
not got this property of self-replication also would be
formed, but while these latter molecules would just
decay in time into simpler molecules, the self-reproducing ones would have the power of endurance. In
this way, more and more of the available atoms would
find their way into the self-reproducing molecules.

Natural Selection

At this stage the development of life must have
hung on a thin thread. Indeed, there were probably
many false starts. But every now and then, one such
molecule might build up into a slightly more complex
molecule. Every new change in the original molecule
that tended to make its power of self-reproduction

more reliable would tend to be perpetuated, at the expense of less "efficient" molecular structures.

This concept of "natural selection" is one of the most important ideas in science, and one that can be applied right through the scale of living things. It was put forward first in a well-argued form just a hundred years ago by Charles Darwin, in his famous book *The Origin of Species*. In the simplest terms, the theory of natural selection says that each generation produces individuals that are in some respect different from their parents. Those individuals whose special peculiarities confer on them some advantage (for example, an added ability to protect themselves from their natural predators, or to find food more efficiently) will tend, on the average, to survive, and pass on their special advantage to their offspring. Changes which confer no such advantage will not have any more tendency to survive than any other "useless" variation, and will eventually die out from the species.

In this way, we may understand how it is that forms of life develop in such a way as to be well suited to their environment. More important still, it allows life to change with changes of the general environment. If such ideas on the origin of life are true, then conditions on the Earth *now* are not suitable for the genesis of life; yet by natural selection life forms have developed that are suited to the new (oxygen-rich) environment, and which would be quite unable to live in the original atmosphere of the Earth.

A hundred years after Darwin's book, there is still argument as to whether the hypothesis of natural selection is fully adequate to explain the wide diversity

of life on Earth. It is true that there are some difficulties in the straightforward application of "natural
selection"—for example, how can it explain the development by stages of an organ that seems to confer
no survival advantages in its primitive stages, but only
when fully developed? But there can be little doubt
that the main concept behind the theory of evolution
is a most powerful aid to our understanding of the
development of life on Earth.

Chance and Environment

There is one very important refinement that has
had to be made since Darwin's day. It is essential to
the theory of evolution that the changes that occur,
and upon which natural selection operates, come
about by chance—that is to say, the environment has
no direct control over which changes occur in *individuals*, but only in the *selection* of advantageous
variations. Now it is obvious that the environment can
affect the growth and development of individuals;
otherwise there would be no point in using fertilizers
to increase a crop yield.

But these variations, due to deficiencies in the environment, are not inherited, for they are not due to
changes in hereditary substance. The children of a
man who has been stunted because of lack of the right
food will, given the right conditions, grow into normal children. But very much more rarely, a peculiarity
in the development of one individual is due to an
actual change in the hereditary substance. Such a

change is called a *mutation*, and it is these mutations
that form the raw material of natural selection. As yet,
we cannot trace the exact changes that occur in the
nucleic-acid molecules, although in a few years' time
this may be possible in some cases. But we do know
(mainly from experiments with flies and other rapidly
reproducing creatures) that such changes can be
caused by increased temperature, and by the absorption of energy from X-rays and ultraviolet light.

The successful development of a species of life will
depend very critically upon the rate of mutation. If
the mutation rate is too high, then a "valuable" mutation will not have time to become established
throughout the species before it is changed into something else, while if the mutation rate is too slow, and
conditions in the environment are changing, the species will not throw up enough variations for natural
selection to have any chance to adapt the species as a
whole to the changing conditions. But again we need
not be surprised to find that in existing species the
natural mutation rate is about right; for by natural
selection those nucleic-acid molecules that had the
wrong mutation rate in the prevailing conditions
would have been eliminated.

Stages of Development

With this perspective on the evolution of life, we
can consider some of the important stages in the development of life on Earth. At first, the (relatively)
simple self-reproducing large molecules would be

quite inert, and would simply wait until currents of wind or water brought the necessary materials for self-reproduction, in the right chemical forms, to them. A clear advantage is gained, however, if the basic molecule becomes surrounded by a storehouse which could serve to process chemically the raw material in the neighborhood of the molecule (under the action of sunlight) into a form suitable to be made into a second basic molecule.

The next most obvious development is for such a single-celled organism to become mobile and move from one place (when the necessary raw material there had been exhausted) to another. As the developing forms of life acquired greater mobility, and spread into a greater variety of places with differing conditions, there would be a need for an increase in the supply of variations upon which natural selection could work. By natural selection a different means of producing variants was developed. This was for the properties of an individual of the next generation to be determined, not by the properties of only a single member of the previous generation (together with such mutations as might occur naturally), but by the properties of *two* individuals of the previous generation. Each individual inherited two nucleic-acid molecules, one from each parent. It clearly increases the rapidity with which new variations can be tried out (since the *combination* of nucleic-acid molecules in an individual is different from the combination in either parent) while being still an efficient means of preserving structures that have proved of evolutionary value. We can see a sort of intermediate stage in certain single-celled creatures. If you looked, with a microscope, at water in which flowers have been left for a long period, you would see a large number of single-celled creatures called paramecium. Like the amoeba, paramecium reproduces by dividing into two, half of the nucleus going to each daughter cell. But paramecium also indulges in the activity of *conjugation*, whereby two individuals exchange with each other half of their nuclei. The two individuals then separate, and may reproduce by dividing shortly afterwards.

It is probable that the early, mobile single-celled creatures developed in the sea, for mobility would be easier to achieve for an *individual* organism in water than on land. In fact, the tissue fluids of all animals (even if they are animals that live wholly on land) are all salt—blood, sweat and tears are salt. This is a strong indication that some important phase in the development of life in its early stages occurred in the sea.

Mobility was not the only advantage that water conferred on developing life. As life forms became more complex, so they involved the co-ordination of more and more chemical processes. Now the rate at which chemical processes occur depends critically upon temperature, and any change of temperature would alter the different chemical processes differently, so that they would no longer be properly co-ordinated. In the sea the range of temperature is less than on land. The sea water acts as a buffer between the organism and changes of temperature on the Earth's surface. Also, water has its solid form less dense than its liquid form at freezing point, so that ice floats on water, and tends to keep the still unfrozen water beneath it warm. In the dinosaurs, which lived on the Earth several millions of years ago, we see the greatest development (in size at least) of water-bound creatures. One of the most striking incidents in the history of life is the sudden disappearance of the dinosaurs; some change (perhaps an extensive drought) on the Earth occurred so quickly that the dinosaurs could not adapt themselves to the new conditions. But away from the shores, under less favorable conditions, while the dinosaurs were growing large, small creatures—the ancestors of modern mammals—had under the stimulus of their harder environment and by natural selection developed in themselves a temperature control, for they had become *warm-blooded*, and so more or less independent of changes in surrounding temperature. The power of natural selection does not stop at producing creatures that have built-in protection from an unsuitable environment; it has also produced creatures that can change their environment to suit their needs. This is the basic evolutionary advantage conferred on any individuals with more than average *intelligence*. With Man an even more important possibility arises. Because of the development, first of speech and then of writing, each generation in a human society can pass on to the next generation, not only the potentialities of development inherent in the physical nature of Man, but also the accumulated experience of previous generations. Instead of having to discover again the basic facts about their environment, each new generation can build upon the experience of its fore-bears. It is this realization of "cultural evolution" (which in the development of Man has all but re-placed the earlier "biological" evolution) that has led to the rapid (if not explosive) increase in Man's ability to mold his environment to his own needs and desires.

IX. THE ADAPTABILITY
OF LIFE

In the early chapters the discussion of the possibility
of life on other planets in the Universe was based
upon a consideration of those properties of the Earth
that seemed to be necessary for the existence of terrestrial life. But in the last chapter we saw how the
process of natural selection will guide the development of life in such a way that it becomes closely
suited to its environment, and will change with
changes in the environment if these happen not too
quickly. The important question now arises: How far
are the conditions that are necessary for life on Earth
merely a reflection of the conditions under which terrestrial life has developed, and how far are they necessary to any form of life? Can we, in fact, set any
limits to the extent to which natural selection can
adapt life to different conditions?

As we shall see in the following chapter, when I
discuss the crucial question of temperature, highly developed forms of life, being more complex chemical

and physical systems, tend to be more sensitive to changes in external conditions. If we look instead at simple forms of life only, even on the Earth we can find impressive evidence for the efficiency of natural selection in adapting life to most extreme conditions.

Some Extreme Examples

For example, we soon find that free oxygen in the atmosphere is by no means necessary for life, even for organisms that make use of oxygen-burning to obtain energy. It has been shown by experiment that certain algae and mosses can live in sealed tubes of sterilized mineral solutions with no dissolved oxygen in them. At first, they live by producing carbon dioxide, until they have built for themselves a carbon-dioxide atmosphere. Under the action of sunlight, they are then able to synthesize oxygen for themselves, and develop a more "normal" life cycle. They can be made to live in this way until all the nutritive medium in which they were growing has been exhausted. They have this power of adaptability, even though they had evolved to their present form in an oxygen atmosphere.

Even the presence of sunlight seems to be unnecessary. There are bacteria that live in large numbers in the soil and that contain no chlorophyll, yet are able to build up the necessary organic chemicals from inorganic material. Their bodies use the chemical energy stored in natural chemical compounds in the soil, especially those containing oxygen. Bacteria have even been found at a depth of 2½ miles in oil-bearing ground; although this is, perhaps, not a very good example as the oil itself originates from plants that lived on the Earth in the remote past.

Other bacteria can live in even more extraordinary situations. In Tuscany there are hot springs containing a high proportion of boracic acid, and the bacillus *Boracicola* is found living in these hot springs. This same bacillus can live in a saturated solution of boracic acid, and even in a 10-per-cent solution of sulphuric acid. But perhaps the most extraordinary case is of some bacteria that can live in a concentrated solution of mercuric chloride (otherwise known as "corrosive sublimate"), a strong poison to most forms of life on Earth.

Water has played an important role in the development of life on Earth, and is a necessity for most living creatures. Nevertheless, life can exist on Earth under conditions of extreme dryness. For example, as winds blow across the high mountains in the Pamirs, the water in them is frozen out to form snowcaps on the mountains and add to the glaciers. In the valleys of the Pamirs, the air is extremely dry, and at noon the humidity drops almost to zero. But alpine plants have evolved to be suited to this dry climate. Even in the Sahara Desert, where the most sensitive instruments cannot detect water in the soil, there are microbes that can collect and use the minute quantities of water that are there.

In all these cases some oxygen is present, either in the air, in water, in minerals in the ground or produced by the organism by photosynthesis. Can life exist without oxygen at all? There are indeed forms of life that do not require oxygen. Parasites that are found in the intestines of higher animals live in an atmosphere of carbon dioxide, methane, hydrogen, and hydrogen sulphide, with no oxygen; but they depend upon their oxygen-burning hosts for their existence. Some bacteria do not use oxygen, but it is not clear whether they also depend upon other forms of life that do use oxygen.

However, it must be remembered that life on the Earth developed in circumstances where water was abundant, and it is not surprising that the dominant forms of life here require water and oxygen. Also, the organisms that live in unusual conditions may have evolved from more normal life forms, by natural selection, so that they, too, might retain the need for oxygen in some form, directly or indirectly. Is there any fundamental limitation to the kind of chemistry that can form a basis for life?

Carbon Compounds

Already, one fundamental limitation has been discovered. Any life process must be based upon the chemical element carbon. Even the simplest of activities that could meaningfully be called "life" is a complex chemical activity, and to prescribe such activity in detail in the chemical code of the hereditary substance, nucleic acid, requires that the nucleic-acid molecule be complex, containing at least several thousand (and in more advanced life forms, several tens of thousands) of individual atoms. Now of all the chemical elements, only carbon has this property of joining up in long chains of (apparently) indefinite length, and so of serving as a basis for life. This association of carbon with life on Earth has long been known. Indeed, the chemistry of carbon compounds is known as *organic* chemistry, although nowadays many "organic" compounds can be built up in the laboratory without the aid of living creatures.

There is, however, no fundamental reason to suppose that the particular chemical reactions used by terrestrial life forms are the only possible basis for living, for these are simply the reactions that happen to be most efficient in using the chemical material available on Earth. Burning with oxygen, for example, is only one of many possible chemical reactions that give out heat when they occur, and any of these others could serve an organism as a source of energy instead of burning, if the organism was so made to utilize them. In the present state of the Earth's atmosphere the bacteria that do not require oxygen are not capable of developing into more complicated creatures, but in another environment (say on Jupiter) they, and not the oxygen-burning forms, might be the start of the main stream of evolution. If we are right in our belief that the primitive atmosphere of the Earth was not unlike the present atmosphere of Jupiter, and that the oxygen in the Earth's atmosphere is in part due to the activity of plant life in the past, then it would seem that by natural selection even the chemical reactions used by developing life might change with time.

Small organisms on Earth can exist under a very wide range of atmospheric pressure. Some fungus molds and bacteria live without any visible harm under pressures of 3000 atmospheres—that is, 3000 times the pressure of the Earth's atmosphere at the ground. Yeast continues to live at 8000 atmospheres. At the other end of the scale, bacteria were found at altitudes of 65,000 feet during the ascent of the balloon *Explorer II* in 1935 (not to be confused with the *Explorer* artificial satellites). At these heights the pressure of the Earth's atmosphere is less than a tenth of an atmosphere; yet the same bacteria, when later placed in a suitable culture medium, grew satisfactorily. Spores and seeds can be kept, in latent form it is true, for long periods in a vacuum.

Even the temperature range for active life used in earlier chapters does not strictly apply to microorganisms; bacteria and even simple plants (algae) are known to live in hot springs at temperatures as high as 190 degrees F, having become adapted to this temperature. In the next chapter, I will consider how fundamental is the temperature limitation to active life.

It seems, then, very difficult to set any limits to the power of life to adapt itself to various conditions. It is true that in extreme conditions on Earth we find only simple forms of life. But this is what we would expect, for these forms have evolved off a main stream of evolution that was fitted to the more normal conditions on Earth; clearly natural selection would lead to the dominant forms of life being those suited to the most common conditions.

We must be careful, however, to distinguish between conditions under which life might be able to originate from non-living matter, and conditions under which life might be able to exist after sufficient time has elapsed for evolution to make the necessary adaptations to the developing forms of life. In considering the evolution of life on Earth, it is difficult not to believe that, in the earliest stages when the first self-reproducing molecules were being formed, life hung on a thread. The power of natural selection is of no avail until this crucial stage is passed, and this crucial stage is a delicate, complex and difficult chemical reaction. But perhaps after all to use the word "difficult" is to be self-centered, for what it means is "difficult in comparison with chemical techniques so far developed by Man"; the chemistry of nature is much more subtle.

The Future of Life on Earth

We have discussed the evolution of life on the Earth. What of its future? As Professor Bondi described it in his book, we now know a great deal about how a star like the Sun generates its energy, and how its structure will change with time. For the last 5000 million years or so, the Sun has been much as it is today, and it will continue much the same for another period of many thousands of millions of years. (I do not intend to speculate upon the effects that evolution may have on life over this long period, except to say that we should not necessarily accept too readily the somewhat Victorian idea of the necessity of continual progress.) But, in time, changes will begin to appear in the Sun. It will gradually become larger, and, although its surface temperature may drop, it will emit more light and heat than it does now. The Earth will become hotter, even hotter than Mercury is now, and all the atmosphere and water will go from the Earth.

Once the Sun starts to evolve towards the Red Giant stage, it will begin to change very rapidly, so rapidly, in fact, that it could outstrip the powers of natural selection to develop existing dominant forms of life suited to the changes. Such forms of life may have to depend, on Earth, on creating an artificial environment that suits them; the planet that gave birth to their ancestors may become a hostile world. As I remarked in a previous chapter, the emergence of intelligence through natural selection took place because the ability of the organism to adapt its surroundings to itself was a quicker way of adaptation than for the organism to adapt itself to its surroundings. But this has the effect of slowing down or stopping the "biological" evolution; can the powers of intelligence to create an artificial environment on the Earth keep pace with the increasingly rapid changes of temperature as the Sun evolves? It is, to my mind, at least a possibility that under these extreme conditions, the present line of evolution might die out, to be replaced by simple organisms whose chemistry will be more suited to the higher temperatures. As yet, we cannot trace the future changes in the Sun with accuracy beyond this point, but we believe that in the end the Sun must finish up as a star very much less luminous than it is now. The Earth would then be as cold as Pluto. But its temperature will have changed from high to low in but a few million years— a very much more rapid change than the gradual rise in temperature over 10,000 million years. Any life that developed during this cooling phase would have to have a much faster rate of evolution than life as we know it.

At the present time, the possibilities of space travel are in the news. I have no doubt that in the foreseeable future, exploration of other planets in the solar system will become possible. It is another question whether such space-trips will ever become widespread, economic propositions for large numbers of human beings. (Only fifty years ago similar doubts might have been expressed about the economic feasibility of air transport—and what is fifty years in 5000 million?) But it is true that one means of preservation of the present line of development of terrestrial life would be for it to move to other parts of the Universe as conditions became unsuitable on Earth. While this might be a means of keeping in the right temperature—a steady outward migration through the solar system as the Sun gets brighter, and an inward migration as the Sun gets fainter—other conditions on the other planets might well be unsuitable. Here again I suspect that the very fact that intelligent life would attempt to adapt the environment to its needs rather than adapt its needs to the environment would be a disadvantage. It might well be not *Homo sapiens* who inherits the planets, but simple spores of life that he has taken, albeit inadvertently, to environments more suited to their evolution than the Earth; a variation, but an effective one, on the hypothesis that life spreads itself through the Universe on meteorites!

X. LIFE ON OTHER PLANETS

In the previous chapter, it was shown that once the simplest living things have been formed, the process of evolution by natural selection can adapt the developing sequence of life to the most diverse conditions of pressure and chemical composition. The most important restriction on active life (as we know it on Earth) was found to be temperature. Temperature clearly plays a fundamental role in the development of life, for it is intimately connected with the question of the stability of a complex molecule, and, as we have seen, life itself depends upon complex molecules. The restriction of active life to a narrow temperature range was an important feature of our earlier discussion of life outside the Earth. (I must again emphasize that this temperature range concerns the temperatures at which the chemical activity of life occurs. A highly developed organism may have evolved a temperature-control system, such as warm blood, to maintain its right temperature in

spite of changes in the surrounding temperature.)
How far is this temperature restriction a fundamental
one?

External Temperature

There are really three quite distinct questions
bound up in one. The first question is this; why does
a living organism require to remain at more or less the
same temperature to live? The answer is clear. A living organism depends upon a number of different
chemical reactions for its activity, and these chemical
reactions must be carefully co-ordinated, each pro-
ceeding at just the right rate. Now all chemical reactions speed up as the temperature is raised, but at
different rates, so that a group of reactions that were
properly co-ordinated at one temperature would not
be so at another temperature. The simpler the organism, the simpler its chemistry; we would expect simple organisms to be less affected by changes of working temperature than complex organisms. Broadly
speaking, this is true; some bacteria can live over a
range of temperature exceeding 100 degrees F,
whereas with Man a change of only a very few degrees in his body temperature can be serious.

Heat Balance

The second question leads on from this. What determines the actual temperature at which an advanced

form of life keeps itself? The answer here is tied up with the way by which an organism frees itself of the heat that it generates by the process of living. The heat generated by the organism tends to heat the organism up, and so upset its chemical balance. Various means have evolved for the organism to free itself of this heat. It may lose heat to its surroundings from the surface of its body either by conduction (especially important for creatures living in the sea), or radiation in the form of long infrared waves. The rate at which the organism loses heat must just balance the rate at which it generates it—if the loss is too small the organism heats up, and if the loss is too great the organism grows cold.

Higher forms of life have developed another method of getting rid of heat, which can be varied automatically by the organism as it changes its rate of energy generation. This is by evaporating a liquid (in practice, water) at the surface of its body, the evaporation of a liquid using up heat. (This is why your finger feels cold if you dip it in a volatile liquid like methylated spirit, and let the liquid evaporate.) When the organism is excessively active, and generating more than its normal heat, it increases the rate of evaporation of liquid from its body surface.

An organism without such means of getting rid of heat at will has to keep its generation of heat in balance with its loss of heat from its body surface by adjusting its rate of living to the surrounding temperature, lying in a stupor in the hot sun, and spending all its time eating in cold weather.

The heat balance of an organism is also an important factor in relation to its growth. Suppose that we have a creature which, at its correct body temperature and normal rate of living, has the proper balance between heat generated and heat lost. Suppose now that we imagine a second creature, exactly the same as the first except that it is twice as big in every dimension—twice as long, twice as broad and twice as thick. Its volume will be then *eight* times the volume of the first creature, and so, at the same relative degree of activity, it will produce eight times as much heat. But its surface area, through which it has to lose heat to its surroundings, is only *four* times as big. A means of losing heat that is adequate for the smaller creature would be quite inadequate for the larger one. (A similar problem arises in designing rocket motors. The problem is to design a cooling system that allows the rocket chamber to be at a high temperature without the structure of the rocket itself melting. A cooling system that works for a small rocket fails for a big one.)

For different types of organism, using the same basic chemistry, the small creatures will spend most of their time eating, to keep their generation of heat up with their relatively large surface loss, while the problem of a large creature is how to get rid of the heat that it generates. The most efficient way of losing heat is probably by conduction of heat in water, which is why the largest mammal, the whale, has developed in the sea.

In plants, which absorb energy from the Sun as the basis of their activity, the problem of heat balance is, in part, tackled by varying the amount of solar radiation that is absorbed. As we saw in Chapter IV, plants at low temperatures on Earth absorb more of the infrared rays of the Sun than plants at moderate temperatures. In very cold situations this increased absorption may spread into the visible red part of the spectrum, making the plants look definitely bluer than "normal." At the other end of the scale, at high temperatures, the plants would reflect more of the infrared and red parts of the spectrum, appearing thereby redder to the eye. In fact, the algae that live in hot springs at temperatures approaching 200 degrees F tend to be bright orange, rather than green.

Working Temperatures of Organisms

The problem of heat balance thus requires that the temperature of an organism does not vary too much, and also that the working temperatures of organisms using more or less the same chemical reactions will be within a fairly narrow range, as we find for life on Earth, which has in all probability developed from a single evolutionary line. Our third question can then be put. Is there any reason why this temperature range should be just that found on Earth, say from 20 degrees F to 140 degrees F? The answer, I think, is no (Fig. 17). This is simply the working range for organisms using chemical reactions like those of earthly life, and natural selection will have insured the development of just those forms of life whose basic chemistry is suited to temperatures on Earth.

It is true that this temperature range covers the

melting point of ice, and that water has played an
important part in terrestrial evolution. But water is
just a part of the environment, like an oxygen atmosphere, and while it may have affected the details of
evolution of life on Earth, there is no good reason to
believe that its absence would prevent the emergence
of life forms suited to a waterless environment.

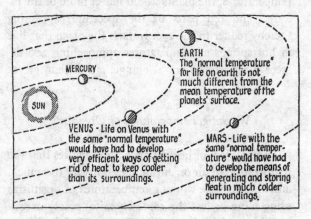

*Fig. 17. Environmental temperature would be criti-
cal in the life processes on different planets.*

At the upper end of the temperature range for active life on Earth, we do approach a fundamental
limit. The higher the temperature, the greater the
likelihood of complex molecules breaking up—for
when a molecule absorbs heat, it is absorbing *disorder*, as we saw in Chapter VII; for any given degree
of complexity of molecular structure, there is an upper temperature limit. Since the complexity of life is,
in fact, the complexity of molecules, this gives an

upper limit to the temperature at which life of a given degree of complexity can develop. Of course, I am not suggesting that life has, on Earth, reached the maximum degree of complexity possible at terrestrial temperatures; evolution has operated over 1000 million years, and for many thousands of millions of years to come, we believe, the temperature of the Earth will be much as it is today.

The lower temperature limit is different, however. As we reduce the temperature, the possible complexity of stable molecules should increase. It is not possible to test this experimentally, for as yet we cannot construct artificially molecules approaching living molecules in complexity, but it is broadly speaking true that as we heat organic molecules up, the more complex ones break up at a lower temperature than the simpler ones. On this basis, then, the *lower* the temperature, the greater the possible complexity of molecules that could form a basis for life forms (with natural selection insuring that those forms that developed were suited to the lower temperatures).

It is true that there is a penalty to pay for the lower temperature. The lower the temperature, the slower the rate of chemical reactions; low-temperature "life" would be much slower than terrestrial life. But "slow" is a purely relative term, meaning slow in comparison with life on Earth. Why, for example, should we consider a life-span of seventy years "normal" throughout the Universe?

The Presence of Life

I am, therefore, inclined to believe that, as far as any fundamental limitation of the development of life is concerned, the lower temperature limit that we used in earlier chapters is of purely local significance. On a planet near a star the potentialities of life are restricted, but those that exist are realized in a (cosmically) short time; on a planet a long way from a star, the potentialities are greater, but the rate of development and evolution is very much slower. If this be true, we should look upon Mars not as an old planet, but as one that is younger than the Earth from the point of view of life—and one whose future developments may far outstrip evolution on the Earth.

This, then, is the general conclusion that emerges from our study of the nature of life, and its relationship to conditions in the Universe. Unless the beginnings of life on Earth were just a "lucky chance" depending upon some very special combination of circumstances about which we know nothing, we can expect life to develop wherever the necessary raw materials are to be found, provided that the temperature is not too high. This means, in practice, upon a planet. Beyond this, there would seem to be no fundamental limit to the ability of life to develop in such a way as to suit its environment. How it would evolve is a much more difficult question. As we look at the history of evolution on Earth, it would seem that time and again some slight variation or peculiarity of the Earth has started evolution off in a particular new direction. The diversity of which the molecular architecture that is life is capable no doubt dwarfs into insignificance the diversity of our imagination.

We can, I think, be certain that the beginning of evolution of life on the Earth—the formation of certain types of complex, "almost living" molecules—was no "lucky chance." On the one hand, we have the evidence of the artificial production of amino acids described in an earlier chapter. More direct evidence has recently come from the analysis of a meteorite. About 1 per cent of the meteorites that are known to have fallen on the Earth contain appreciable amounts of carbon. Very refined chemical analysis, using the latest techniques and instruments, has shown (in the one case that has been analyzed in this way) that the carbon atoms in the meteorite are linked together in molecules which are at least 15 carbon atoms long, and possibly longer. These are already quite complex molecules, and it was found that the properties of these meteoric molecules are very similar to the properties of cytosine, one of the fundamental nucleotides of nucleic acid. While the techniques available do not allow of a definite identification with cytosine, it is clear that elsewhere in the solar system, long-chain carbon molecules that could serve as a basis for the development of living organisms already exist. (There is no possibility that the meteorite picked up these molecules in its passage through the Earth's atmosphere, for the outer layers of the meteorite would become too hot. This does not, however, prevent the possibility of complex molecules surviving within the meteorite, as the heat generated by contact with the atmosphere does not have time to penetrate into the main body of the meteorite.) It is not certain whether meteorites have always been small bodies, remnants of the "planetesimals" out of which the planets may have been formed by accretion, or whether they are the debris from a once-complete planet that exploded; the internal structure of meteorites rather favors the latter idea. In the former case we must suppose that some natural (i.e., inorganic) process (probably associated with the absorption of sunlight) can synthesize such long-chain molecules. On the latter hypothesis, however, it is possible that the long-chain molecules found in this meteorite are themselves the result of living processes on the now-exploded planet.

XI. THE CHEMISTRY OF THE UNIVERSE

In the preceding chapters, we have built up gradually a picture of life as a typical kind of chemical activity, depending upon the properties of particular kinds of complex chemical molecules. In drawing upon this insight into the nature of life as we discussed the possibility of life's existing elsewhere in the Universe, we have assumed tacitly that the particular types of atoms that are required to build up a living molecule exist elsewhere in the Universe, and are available for collection into suitable molecules. (This is, of course, a very much more fundamental assumption than the assumption that the same chemical *reactions* are used by life everywhere; we have suggested that this latter assumption is by no means necessary to the discussion.) But have we any right to assume that the stuff of which the Universe as a whole is made is basically similar to the material of the Earth? Might not the stars be made of quite different atoms, of which we on Earth know nothing? Are we right in assuming that because on the Earth only carbon can form complex long-chain molecules, in the Universe there are no other atoms capable of a similar amalgamation?

Now we can make a direct chemical analysis of some matter from outside the Earth. This is matter that falls from space onto the Earth in the form of meteorites. In meteorites we find the same elements we find in the Earth's crust, in roughly the same proportions and forming similar compounds; in fact, the material within a meteorite usually can be fitted reasonably well into the system of classification of minerals found in the Earth's crust, although there are differences of composition that enable a skilled chemist to distinguish between meteoritic and terrestrial minerals.

This similarity is not really unexpected, for such knowledge as we have about the orbits of meteorites before they encounter the Earth shows that meteorites come from within the solar system. At one time it was thought that the asteroids and meteorites came from a single planet that broke into pieces, and the internal structure of meteorites points to their having been at one time part of a large body. However, if one accepts present theories that the planets were built up from smaller bodies or "planetesimals" by accretion, there is less reason to believe in the former existence of a tenth planet between Jupiter and Mars.

We can obtain this precise knowledge about the chemical composition of meteorites because we can handle them in the laboratory. What about the stars, which we can never touch, but only observe? There seems to be a deep psychological reason why people attach a greater reliability to the sense of touch than to the sense of sight. Because we cannot experiment with the stars, many people find the whole of astrophysics "speculative." Yet, while the fact that astronomy is an observational science imposes special difficulties upon it, and molds astronomical techniques, there is no reason why the sense of sight should be considered less reliable than the sense of touch. When a chemist makes a straightforward chemical analysis of some unknown material, he is, in effect, comparing the chemical properties of the atoms of the unknown material with the chemical properties of known atoms. In a similar way, when an astronomer makes a chemical analysis of the atmosphere of a star, he compares the *optical* properties of atoms in the star's atmosphere (i.e., the ways in which the atoms absorb and emit light) with the optical properties of known atoms on the Earth. To do this, he passes the light of the star through a *spectrograph*.

Astrophysics and the Spectrograph

In this instrument the image of the star in a telescope falls on a slit, through which the starlight passes (Fig. 18). The beam of starlight then passes through a lens which turns it into a parallel beam of light. This beam passes through a prism of glass which has the ability to bend the beam of light. But the amount by which it bends the beam depends upon the color of the light, red light being bent least and violet light most. After passing through a second, focusing lens, the light forms a series of images of the entrance slit, the images in different colors lying side by side to form a *spectrum*, which is then photographed.

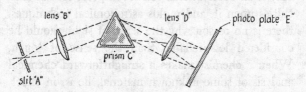

Fig. 18. The arrangement of slit, lenses and prism of a spectrograph for analyzing light is illustrated here.

If the light of a hot body (for example, the filament of an electric-light bulb) is passed through a spectrograph, the spectrum that it gives is a continuous band (like a rainbow) with all colors present (Fig. 19). On the other hand, the light from a discharge tube (for example, a neon sign) or a flame gives a spectrum with only a limited number of colors present. The separate images of the slit in these definite colors show up in the spectrum as a series of bright lines. Furthermore, the particular combinations of colors that appear in the spectrum are characteristic of the particular atoms that are present in the discharge tube.

The spectrum of a typical star is different again, for it appears as an *absorption-line spectrum*—a continuous colored band with certain colors missing, giving the appearance of dark lines in the spectrum.

We can produce a similar spectrum in the laboratory by passing the continuous spectrum from a hot source through a gas at a lower temperature. The dark lines appear in the spectrum in just the same positions as the bright lines in the spectrum of the same gas when heated. So the spectrum of a star tells us not only which atoms are present in the atmosphere of the star, but, also, that the matter in the star gets hotter as we go inside the star.

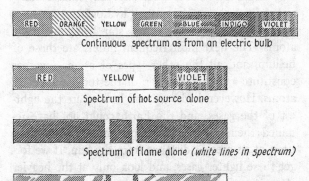

Continuous spectrum as from an electric bulb

Spectrum of hot source alone

Spectrum of flame alone *(white lines in spectrum)*

Spectrum of light from a very hot source passing through flame producing black lines in spectrum

Fig. 19. Different types of spectra.

There is another way in which we can learn about the chemical composition of a star. We can use the known laws of physics to build up a mathematical model of a star, in which the temperature, pressure and density of the matter inside the star at any level can be found in terms of the mass, luminosity, radius and temperature of the actual star. It turns out that the possible combinations of mass, luminosity, radius and temperature for a single star depend rather critically upon some aspects of its chemical composition, so that it is now possible for us to tell the proportion of hydrogen, helium and heavier elements throughout the star from its physical appearance.

At first sight, the chemical composition of a star is so different from the chemical composition of the Earth or a meteorite that it seems impossible that they could have come from originally similar material. A normal star is almost all hydrogen, over 90 per cent of the atoms in such a star being hydrogen atoms. The next most frequent atoms are those of helium, and all the other types of atoms together constitute a minute fraction of the total number of atoms. However, hydrogen and helium are the lightest of the gases, and the Earth could not have retained them as an atmosphere for an appreciable time, at its present distance from the Sun. If we forget these lighter gases, and look only at the heavier atoms, we find that the relative proportions of the different elements are very similar in all bodies for which we have any chemical knowledge—i.e., the Earth, meteorites and stars. It looks reasonable to suppose that stars and planets can have condensed out of similar material, the smaller planets losing their hydrogen and helium during or after their formation.

Atomic Structure

Attempts have been made to understand why the chemical composition of matter in the Universe should be just as it is. An atom of even the simplest chemical element, hydrogen, is a complex system, consisting of a positively charged nucleus (a *proton*) with a single negatively charged *electron* moving around it like a tiny planet about a tiny sun. Fig. 20 is a great simplification, but it will suffice for our present purpose. The electron can move only in certain definite orbits; when it jumps from one orbit to another nearer to the proton, the atom emits a pulse of light in one of the typical hydrogen spectrum lines, and when the electron jumps the other way, the atom absorbs a pulse of light. The optical and chemical properties of the hydrogen atoms depend upon the particular possible orbits for the electron.

The proton is nearly two thousand times heavier than the electron. We may think of all normal atoms as built up out of electrons, protons and *neutrons* (a particle as heavy as the proton, but with no electric charge). For example, the nucleus of a normal helium atom consists of two protons and two neutrons. Having a net positive charge of two units, the helium nucleus can hold two orbital electrons to make up the neutral helium atom. The great differences between the chemical properties of helium and hydrogen are due entirely to the fact that one atom has a single electron and the other a pair. The normal carbon atom has a nucleus consisting of six protons and six neutrons, with six orbital electrons.

It is the structure of the nucleus that is all-impor-

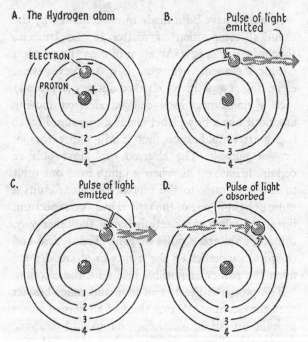

Fig. 20. *A greatly simplified concept of the hydrogen atom and the relation between the orbit of its one electron and the absorption or emission of light.*

tant, for it determines the number of electrons that the atom can contain. At temperatures of a few thousand degrees centigrade, the atoms of a gas collide violently enough for the outer electrons to be knocked off, the gas becoming ionized; but the nuclei remain intact. But at temperatures of about 15 million degrees centigrade, which we find at the centers of normal stars, the nuclei themselves collide with sufficient violence for changes to occur in them. One important reaction of this sort, the one that provides the source of light and heat of the Sun, is for protons (nuclei of hydrogen atoms) to fuse together to form nuclei of helium atoms.

The Formation of Elements

Since all atomic nuclei are composed of protons and neutrons, we can try to discover under what conditions a collection of protons and neutrons would aggregate into nuclei of atoms in just the proportions that we find among the atoms in the Universe. It turns out that it is rather difficult to find the right conditions. One theory supposes that many thousands of millions of years ago the Universe was much smaller, denser and hotter than it is today. As we will see in the next chapter, this view is consistent with a general tendency to expansion that we see in the Universe today. In the early stages of such an expanding universe, conditions were suitable for the formation of nuclei of heavy elements out of protons and neutrons, but to get the observed distribution it has to be supposed that the initial expansion was at just the right rate, slow enough to allow heavy nuclei to form, but fast enough to prevent the distribution of nuclei among the different types from adjusting itself completely to the falling temperature. It seems that no single temperature can account for the present distribution of nuclei.

Another theory, and one that has proved more fruitful, is that the heavy elements are formed out of hydrogen throughout the Universe all the time. The places where these heavy nuclei are built up are the centers of stars. The theory is far from being worked out in detail yet, but the following outline gives an idea of the process (Fig. 21). A star begins as a condensation in interstellar matter, which we take to be at first pure hydrogen. As it contracts under its own gravitation, the center becomes hotter, until it reaches the temperature where hydrogen nuclei fuse into helium nuclei. For a time which depends upon the mass of the star, but which is measured in millions of years, the star shines more or less steadily as the helium is formed.

However, the time will come when the hydrogen begins to become exhausted. This will occur first near the center of the star, and the star acquires an exhausted core of helium, at the same time expanding and becoming a Red Giant star. When the available hydrogen has been used up, the star cannot keep distended, and it begins again to contract under its own gravitation, the central temperature rising again. When it reaches about 100 million degrees C, a new nuclear reaction begins—helium is converted into carbon. By now the evolution of the star is very rapid, and so, although every star may, at some time in its life, pass through a helium-burning phase, the proportion of stars actually burning helium at any one time will be very small. Models of helium-burning stars are still rather uncertain.

What happens after this is uncertain, but, presumably, when the available helium has been exhausted, the star will again contract, and the central temperature again rise. When it reaches about 1000 million degrees C, new thermonuclear reactions be-

Fig. 21. The life history of a star: (A) condensation of interstellar matter; (B) contraction and heating; (C) expansion and surface cooling; (D) further contraction with creation of heavy elements; (E) explosion into supernova with dispersion of material into space.

come possible, with nuclei of heavy elements such as magnesium, silicon, etc., being formed. This process will continue, step by step, and at an ever-increasing rate, until all the heavy elements have been formed. The evolution, now, would be so rapid that the star would become unstable and explode, sending its material out into interstellar space to join the interstellar hydrogen already there. We see such exploding stars—we call them *supernovae*. While many details of this theory remain to be worked out, I think that in its general outline it is rather convincing. It serves not only to explain the distribution of atoms in the Universe among the various elements, but also to explain certain differences from one star to another.

Stars with a very small content of heavy elements may be thought of as first-generation stars formed out of almost pure hydrogen; stars with a higher proportion of heavy elements (of which the Sun is one) are second-generation stars formed out of interstellar matter that has already been enriched with heavy elements by the explosion of first-generation stars. If this theory be true, then the atoms of the ground on which you walk, the atoms of the paper on which this book is printed—indeed, the atoms of which you and I are made—were, in the remote past, formed inside a star! As yet, we do not know how near to the truth this theory is. But, true or not, we can be sure of one thing, simply on the basis of our observations of the spectra of stars. The Earth is not in any way peculiar as regards the material of which it is made. Whether planets are common throughout the Universe, or rare, we can be sure that wherever a planet is formed, it will contain the basic elements necessary for the development of life. In this respect, if in no other, the assumptions that we have made up till now are not at fault. There remain the theories of the evolution of the Universe, and we shall conclude this book with a discussion of them.

XII. THE EVOLUTION OF THE UNIVERSE

We have seen how we may view the formation of the elements out of hydrogen inside the stars. It was a tentative view, to be sure, but one that holds at this time considerable promise of further development. In this theory, stars condense out of interstellar matter in several stages, at each stage converting simpler elements into heavier ones, and finally exploding their material into space, to enrich the hydrogen already there with heavy elements. Out of this enriched interstellar matter, new stars condense; and so on. Somehow in the process, planets are formed out of material that was originally inside a star of an earlier generation. New planets—possible sites for the development of life—are thus forming in the Universe today. Will conditions in the Universe remain always suitable for the formation of planets, with stars to keep them at moderate temperatures? Or must the Universe itself submit to the second law of thermodynamics and decay to a static uniformity?

If we are to look at life in the Universe on the scale of time as well as distance, this is a crucial point.

In the wide spectrum of different theories of the origin and evolution of the Universe, there is a sharp division. This division is between theories that believe that the Universe is evolving and decaying, and those that believe that, although individual objects (stars, galaxies, etc.) evolve, the Universe as a whole remains in a steady state. But before I discuss these theories, I would like to say something about an earlier (and now totally discarded) picture of the Universe current in the Middle Ages, and associated with the name of Aristotle, because it points the problem.

The Aristotelian System

In the Aristotelian system the Earth was the center of the Universe, Earth being one of the four basic "elements." The other three, water, air and fire, were arranged in concentric spheres about the Earth in that order—these were their proper places. If any of the elements were disturbed, then they automatically found their way back to their rightful sphere. A clod of earth thrown into the air falls back; water that has got into the air in clouds falls back to the Earth's surface as rain; and the flame from a fire burning on the Earth seems to rise upwards into the sky. Above the sphere of fire were the Moon, Sun, planets and stars, carried around the Earth in daily, complicated orbits by a complex system of crystalline spheres.

Now this system did serve to explain many of the

features of the behavior of moving objects in everyday life. But there was a contrast between terrestrial matter and the Moon, Sun and stars, for the celestial bodies did not fall to the ground, but continued forever in their orbits about the Earth. To Aristotle all matter above the sphere of the Moon was different *in kind* from matter on the Earth; while terrestrial matter decayed and fell down, celestial matter was unchanging and eternal. Even if things terrestrial were ephemeral, there was the promise of an eternal existence for the Universe itself. The Sun-centered systems of Copernicus and Kepler robbed the Earth of its uniqueness—the planets too were like the Earth, and so must decay. And if the planets, why not the stars and the Sun? Cold comfort here.

Galileo and Newton broke down the barrier between terrestrial and celestial matter by showing that the same laws of motion that govern the falling of a body on Earth also govern the motion of the planets (including the Earth) about the Sun. Modern methods of astrophysics show conclusively that the matter of which the stars are made is composed of the same atoms as matter on Earth. Must we then accept the conclusion that the Universe itself is doomed to decay?

Theories of the Universe

At first sight, it would seem that we must, and some support is given to this notion by the fact that the whole Universe seems to be expanding and dissipating. When we look at the light of distant systems of stars, we find that the spectrum lines with which we are familiar are shifted systematically to the red, and the more distant the galaxy, the greater the red shift. The only explanation that laboratory physics can give for such a red shift is that it is due to a

Galaxies rushing away from each other, finally dying and depopulating the universe

Fig. 22. Dispersion of galaxies.

velocity of recession. If the red shift is indeed a velocity shift, then all the galaxies are rushing away from each other, and the density of the Universe must be getting smaller and smaller and smaller, to finish up as a vacuum! (Fig. 22). It is true that this expansion does not apply to individual galaxies, but only to the distances between them. But this is small respite, for stars themselves, by gradually converting the available nuclear fuel into heavy elements, must eventually die out altogether (Fig. 23).

According to this picture the Universe began

(some tens of thousands of millions of years ago) as a very small, very dense, and very hot system which rapidly expanded, and continues to expand. If this be true, then very distant galaxies (which, because light has a finite velocity, we see as they were a long time ago) should appear to us to be closer together in space.

Fig. 23. According to one theory, galaxies, much like stars, are formed from interstellar material, grow in brightness and in time burn out.

Other theories deny that the Universe as a whole is evolving. Instead, they postulate that while individual stars and galaxies evolve and die away, new matter appears and forms new galaxies and the Universe as a whole remains in a steady state. If this be so, then the Universe at great distances (i.e., at great times in the past) should appear the same as the

Universe nearby in its general aspects. Recent radio observations of the numbers of very distant galaxies seem to confirm the "explosive" picture of the Universe, but until the interpretation of these observations has been more closely scrutinized, the case against the steady-state theories is still "not proven."

Do these theories conflict with the general law about decrease of order (the second law of thermodynamics) which we discovered from terrestrial physics, and which I discussed in Chapter VII? Not necessarily, for this law applies only to a closed system, isolated from its surroundings. A living organism *appears* to defy the law, but only because it takes in order from its surroundings. If the organism and its surroundings are taken together, then the order of the whole system does decrease, although the order of *part* of the system (the living organism) may remain fixed or increase. The important question is whether the Universe as a whole can be considered a closed system in this sense. If the Universe is infinite, it is doubtful whether the second law can be properly applied to it at all.

This is another dichotomy in theories of the Universe—is the Universe finite in extent, or infinite? A finite Universe cannot have any *edge* with space beyond. Space itself must be bounded, as the surface of the Earth is bounded. The surface of the Earth has no edge—if you walked in a straight line in any direction, you would come back eventually to where you started, provided that you stayed on the two-dimensional surface of the Earth. In the closed Universe, in whichever direction you went in a "straight line" in three dimensions, you would come back to where you started without finding any edge.

It is difficult to picture such a Universe—but no more difficult, I think, than to picture a Universe infinite in extent. For if the Universe were infinite in extent, must not every possible arrangement of atoms occur an infinite number of times? Would there not be, on an infinite number of planets, an infinite number of people reading an infinite number of different books on Life by an infinite number of authors? This would be true only if the number of possible arrangements of atoms was itself finite—and of this we cannot be sure. But while a discussion of the infinity of the Universe may be useful in the context of cosmology, it is idle to speculate about the differences between individual objects or events in such an infinite Universe, for we can never hope to observe more than an infinitesimal fraction of them. I will say no more about infinity.

Science and Speculation

We must be careful to distinguish between "speculation" and "idle speculation." While the latter has no place in science, the former, far from being alien to science, is its very lifeblood. To a greater or lesser degree, all scientific theories are "speculative." Indeed, the more fundamental and far-reaching a scientific theory is, the more speculative it is likely to be when first formulated. It is a totally erroneous belief that science is concerned with "pure facts" (whatever a pure fact may be). The mere accumulation of facts is a very primitive form of science. A mature science seeks to arrange the facts in significant patterns, to see relationships between hitherto unrelated aspects of the Universe, to put forward hypotheses that serve to give insight into the patterns so discovered, and, most important, to suggest new observations or experiments. A postulate that is not speculative—that is to say, a theory that does not suggest new ways of looking at the Universe—is unlikely to be an important contribution to the development of science.

What is important in science is that, wherever possible, theories are subjected to check by new observations or experiments. One of the difficulties in astronomy is that frequently the observations required to test a theory cannot be obtained for practical reasons (such as the lack of light, grasp of telescopes, or the absorption of the Earth's atmosphere). I do not think that for this reason astronomers should not formulate theories; for until a theory has been formulated, it is not possible to know whether or not any crucial observations are possible. And without an active theoretical structure, astronomy, no less than any other science, would stagnate. It is necessary, however, to make sure that wherever possible theoretical speculation is tied to observation. Much of what I have had to say in this book is, of necessity, speculative. But I hope and believe that the attempt to examine the place of life in the Universe on the basis of our knowledge of astronomy and biology is not *idle* speculation.

In this attempt, I have had to trespass upon fields in which I am not an expert. Yet in an age of specialization it is important that occasionally some attempts are made to bridge the gaps between the sciences, and to create some broader picture. My colleagues in the biological and chemical sciences (to whose patience in frequent discussions I am much in debt) will, I hope, agree with me at least in this.

In short, then, I think that the naïve view, which concentrates on the peculiar necessities of life on Earth and sees life as having a precarious hold in a Universe at best neutral to life and at worst hostile to it, is in error. Bearing in mind what we now know about the fundamental nature of life and its ability to adapt itself (by natural selection) to a variety of environments, we can set only much broader limits to the possibility of life elsewhere in the Universe. While life on or in a star, or on a planet very close to a star, may be impossible, we would be unwise to rule out the possibility of its existence on any other planet. I see life—yes, even intelligent life—as a normal manifestation of matter in the Universe, just as a star or a galaxy is.

In conclusion I would like to consider three points which I have found, in conversation, to trouble the non-scientist. Does not the great size of the Universe which modern astronomy reveals make human life seem insignificant and unimportant? I do not think so. We must be careful not to equate size with importance or significance. To me, it is not so much the size of the Universe that is significant, as the fact that human beings, from their limited position on the

Earth (a tiny speck of dust in the cosmos), can nevertheless talk about the Universe as a whole, and attempt (however imperfectly) to understand it.

To some people, the scientific analysis of the nature of life seems somehow to remove the sense of
"wonder" that might be considered appropriate to it.
Again, I cannot agree, for respect is not the preroga-
tive of ignorance. An African bushman presented
with his first sight of a television screen might "wonder" at pictures in a box. But this sentiment is ephemeral, and it soon dissipates with familiarity. On
the other hand, to know how a television picture is
produced is to induce (in me, at least) a profound
respect for the ingenuity of the many scientists and
technologists who have made the finished product
possible. This is a respect refined and tempered by
knowledge, and is the more enduring. In a similar
way, as we learn more about the complex chemical
architecture that is life, I find my own sense of wonder not decreasing but increasing.

The other difficulty is that the sense of purpose,
which is so important to us as human beings, seems
to be lacking in the picture. It may be, of course, that
the sense of purpose arises in living creatures for no
more profound a reason than the obvious necessity
to keep alive. But even if you reject this explanation,
then I still see no reason why natural selection itself
could not be a tool for the realization of purpose in
the Universe. Again, if the Universe is evolving towards a state of decay, when no life will be possible,
this does not seem to me to deny the significance to
the development of life within its limited time span.

A Beethoven symphony would be no less meaningful if it were never played again; its significance lies in the playing and the listening, and not in the possibility that it might be played again in the future.

But these are matters that cannot be discussed within the framework of science, for science can neither define purpose, nor recognize it in the Universe if it exists. Of course, the picture of life and the Universe given by the scientist is only part of the whole picture. The psychologist, the sociologist, the philosopher would have different pictures to paint. In doing so, each of them would see an image of himself as in a prism—a complicated prism, with many faces making up the whole. I have, perforce, been looking into only one face of the prism—but it is enough.

INDEX